CIVILIZATION

ESSO presents

Civilization: Ancient Treasures from the British Museum

Dr Timothy Potts

Australian National Gallery, Canberra, 24 March to 11 June 1990

Museum of Victoria, Melbourne, 28 June to 23 September 1990

Provision of indemnification by the Australian Government through the Department of the Arts, Sport, the Environment, Tourism and Territories.

Acknowledgements

The author is grateful to the following for assistance in the preparation of this catalogue:

The officers of the Departments of Coins and Medals, Egyptian Antiquities, Greek and Roman Antiquities, Prehistoric and Romano-British Antiquities, and Western Asiatic Antiquities in the British Museum.

Dr J.A. Black
Professor Sir John Boardman
Dr J. Malek
Dr P.R.S. Moorey
Dr R. Parkinson
Mr E. Robinson
Dr J. Spier
Dr G. Vaughan
Dr H. Whitehouse.

Photography: Christi Graham, P. Hayman, I. Kerslake, P.E. Nicholls, Brian Tremain, Barbara Winter (British Museum).

All illustrations of works from **Civilization** are © the Trustees of the British Museum.

Produced by the Publications Department of the Australian National Gallery.

Cataloguing-in-publication data

Civilization: Ancient Treasures from the British Museum.

ISBN 0 642 13041 8.

1. British Museum — Exhibitions. 2. Middle East — Antiquities — Exhibitions. 3. Greece — Antiquities — Exhibitions. 4. Italy — Antiquities — Exhibitions. I. Potts, Timothy, 1958– II. Australian National Gallery.

930.10749471

The objects included in this catalogue are on loan from the British Museum.

Typeset by Brown & Co. Typesetters Pty Ltd, Canberra
Printed by Inprint Limited, Brisbane

The Australian National Gallery gratefully acknowledges the support of Qantas Airways Limited, Nine Network and WIN Television.

(cover)
King Ashurnasirpal II hunting lions
Assyrian palace relief
cat. no. **8**

The opening of the Australian National Gallery in 1982 has made a great change to the cultural makeup of Australia. The presence of the Gallery provided not only a building to house the National Collection, but also an institution capable of providing great cultural experiences for all Australians. In addition to its active outreach programs, bringing its collections in many different ways to communities all over Australia, the Gallery regularly has provided major exhibitions from collections of great repute, both organizing them and touring them to other capital cities within Australia. As an adjunct to these exhibitions, the Gallery, through its extensive publications and marketing programs, produces fine publications, posters and other products that serve to reinforce the experience of these great occasions.

In the past we have been graced with **The Entombed Warriors** from China, **The Great Impressionists** from the Courtauld Institute of Art, London, **Twentieth-Century Masters** from The Metropolitan Museum of Art, New York, and **Old Masters — New Visions** from The Phillips Collection in Washington DC. Now we have one of the most important collections of antiquities in the world from the British Museum in London. **Civilization: Ancient Treasures from the British Museum** marks the first time that such a collection from the British Museum has been offered as a complete exhibition. As Minister for the Arts it gives me great pleasure to be able to offer the indemnification for the exhibition on behalf of the Australian Government. Through its indemnification scheme the government makes it possible for major exhibitions like this to be available to the Australian people.

I would like to thank the sponsors of the exhibition for providing valuable support. Esso Australia Ltd, the major commercial sponsor, has extended to the Gallery the finances necessary to make this large undertaking possible. Qantas Airways Limited has provided invaluable support through its freight and courier arrangements for bringing the treasures of the British Museum to Australia. Special thanks go to the Nine Network and WIN Television for their generous support in marketing the exhibition.

It is generally understood that any nation or culture is measured, in time, by its achievements in science, philosophy and art. These are the measuring sticks of great civilizations. It is important that Australia has the opportunity to view these ancient treasures in its own environment; to bring home, as it were, the cultural influences that shaped the present manifestations of Western civilization in Australia. Such an exhibition opens the way for renewed examination of other influences on Australia's development including those of Asia and the Pacific basin.

I commend the Australian National Gallery's initiative in developing the concept for **Civilization: Ancient Treasures from the British Museum**, the British Museum for its willingness to lend these supremely beautiful objects and the judgement of Esso Australia Ltd, Qantas Airways Limited and the Nine Network and WIN Television for sponsoring the exhibition. The Australian public will be offered a unique and exciting experience as a result of this collaboration.

The Hon. Clyde Holding, MP
Minister for Arts, Tourism and Territories

Esso is delighted to join the Australian National Gallery in bringing to you this unique and memorable exhibition **Civilization: Ancient Treasures from the British Museum**.

Our sponsorship has particular significance at this time because it coincides with the twentieth anniversary of the sale of crude oil from Bass Strait, an event which marked a major step forward for Esso and the Australian community. Our sponsorship of this major exhibition also provides us with an ideal opportunity to reaffirm our continuing commitment to the Australian community to make a substantial contribution to the quality of life of all Australians through our business activities and our support for cultural and community programs.

Civilization: Ancient Treasures from the British Museum is the first complete exhibition of ancient material ever lent by the British Museum. The exhibition covers the rise of the great civilizations of the Middle East and the Mediterranean basin and brings together some of the finest and best known artefacts in the world. Their exquisite beauty as art objects, and their testimony to the advanced level of those cultures credited with providing the basis of Western civilization, will provide interest and enjoyment to all who view them.

Civilization will be on exhibition at the Australian National Gallery and will also be seen at the Museum of Victoria in Melbourne.

We congratulate the Council and staff of the Australian National Gallery for organizing this fine exhibition, and join them in paying tribute to those who made it possible. In particular, we join the Gallery in thanking the Hon. Clyde Holding, Minister for the Arts, Tourism and Territories, and the Australian Government for providing their support for the indemnification of the works, without which the Australian tour would not have been possible. We would also like to extend our appreciation to the British Museum for providing the splendid works on display, and to James Mollison, former Director of the Australian National Gallery, who conceived of the exhibition.

John M. Schubert
Chairman and Managing Director
Esso Australia Ltd.

Foreword

This exhibition includes a number of the finest works from the collection of an institution that is universally acknowledged as not only the world's greatest treasure house of objects but also an historical repository of the artefacts and documents of civilizations dating from prehistory to the present.

As one of the oldest museums in the world, the British Museum has developed its vast and extraordinary collections over a period of 230 years, and much of the work that has been carried out by the Museum has been pioneering in its own time. Many precious objects owe their survival today to the efforts of those who have been collectors for the Museum.

With a few exceptions, the works in this exhibition are of such importance that they have formed part of the Museum's permanent display for decades. It is therefore remarkable that this material has been made available to travel to Australia. Conscious of the fact that it would not be possible in this day and age, even with unlimited funds, to put together a collection of such depth and breadth, the Australian National Gallery, as organizer of this exhibition, and the Museum of Victoria are delighted to be able to bring such a collection to Australia. Hundreds of thousands of Australians who have not had the good fortune to view these antiquities in the British Museum in London will now have the opportunity to see and enjoy these great works of art in the Australian National Gallery, Canberra, and the Museum of Victoria in Melbourne.

Although, as the title indicates, the works in the exhibition are regarded as 'treasures' of the British Museum, this exhibition was not conceived as a random sample of beautiful objects from its collections. Each piece has been carefully selected so that as a whole the exhibition tells something of the story of civilization as it emerged around the shores of the Mediterranean from 3500 BC to AD 300.

It would not have been possible to bring this exhibition to the people of Australia without the generosity of the trustees of the British Museum and its director Sir David Wilson, and the enthusiastic support of the deputy director Jean Rankine. Special thanks are due to her and to Dr Timothy Potts who put so much time and effort into selecting the works for the show, negotiating with British Museum keepers and preparing the catalogue. We would also like to thank the following Keepers, from whose care the works in this exhibition were released: Mr T.C. Mitchell and Dr J.E. Curtis, Department of Western Asiatic Antiquities; Mr B.F. Cook, Department of Greek and Roman Antiquities; Dr V. Davies, Department of Egyptian Antiquities; Dr I. Longworth, Department of Prehistoric and Romano-British Antiquities; Dr J. Kent, Department of Coins and Medals.

We would also like to acknowledge the outstanding vision of the former Director of the Australian National Gallery, Mr James Mollison, who conceived the exhibition and carried through the early negotiations which have resulted in a show of the highest quality.

We hope that the works presented in this exhibition and the history they record, together with the accompanying catalogue, will create a lasting impression on the many visitors who come to admire and take pleasure in a wonderful collection of antiquities that is unlikely to be seen in Australia again for a very long time.

Elizabeth Churcher
Director
Australian National
Gallery

Bob Edwards
Director
Museum of Victoria

Contents

Preface

In an institution over two and a quarter centuries old, it is rare for any one event to change established traditions, but this exhibition is without precedent in the history of the British Museum.

The British Museum lends a great deal: at any one time, several hundred objects from its collections will be on show in, or en route to, several dozen museums and galleries in various parts of the world, either as contributions to temporary exhibitions drawn from multiple sources or to complement the permanent collections of the borrower. On rare occasions, complete exhibitions have been assembled by one of my colleagues for loan overseas, but these have usually been from the Department of Prints and Drawings and therefore made up of items that are both relatively portable and barred for conservation reasons from permanent exhibition. The removal from permanent display in the British Museum's galleries of large stone or bronze sculptures — including two pieces weighing well over a tonne each — and their transport to a country thousands of kilometres away, together with tiny coins, sealstones and jewellery, and a fragile national treasure like the Mildenhall Dish, is an exercise of a totally different order.

The inspiration for the present exhibition came from James Mollison, former Director of the Australian National Gallery; it was he who proposed that we should present for the Australian public an exhibition which was not only from the British Museum but of the British Museum, an exhibition which would convey the essence of the experience of visiting the great neo-classical building in central London to an audience on the other side of the world.

The British Museum was conceived by the architect Sir Robert Smirke in a style and to a scale to house the monumental sculpture and other art of the ancient civilizations of the Mediterranean world, the heritage we share with all Australians of European extraction. Dr Timothy Potts worked with my colleagues in five departments to select from the finest objects in the Museum's collections an exhibition of sculpture, pottery, metalwork and other antiquities from the ancient Near East, Egypt, Greece and the Roman Empire, and thus to provide a glimpse of the development of that common heritage.

I should like to thank James Mollison and his colleagues in Canberra and Melbourne for the five years of fruitful collaboration which led to the realization of **Civilization: Ancient Treasures from the British Museum**, and, in particular, our thanks are due to Dr Potts for his painstaking work on the selection of objects and their presentation in this catalogue.

David Wilson
Director
British Museum

The Story of the British Museum

The 'father' of the British Museum was Sir Hans Sloane (1660–1753), a fashionable physician and obsessive collector who lived in eighteenth-century London. During the course of a long and active life, Sloane amassed the largest and most varied collection of objects of scientific, historical and artistic interest in Britain — some 80 000 'plants, fossils, minerals, zoological, anatomical and pathological specimens, antiquities and artificial curiosities, prints, drawings and coins, books and manuscripts'. In his will Sloane offered all this to the nation for the modest sum of £20 000, to be paid to his daughters. Although this was only a fraction of the collection's real cost, King George II declared the Exchequer too poor to meet Sloane's terms, and it was only when Parliament, after much deliberation, voted to raise the money by public lottery that the Museum's future was secured. Montagu House, on the site of the present museum building in Bloomsbury, was chosen to house the collection, and by 15 January 1759 all was ready for the first regular visitors to be admitted.

The extraordinary breadth of Sloane's collection and the terms of its bequest assured the newly born British Museum a special place in museum history. Sloane had stipulated that his collections should be housed intact and made freely accessible to the public. Although not the oldest museum in Britain, it was arguably the first major public museum anywhere in Europe open free of charge to all 'studious and curious persons' who might wish to see it, and which aimed, in principle, at universality. In the eclectic spirit of the day, Sloane's collection had found a place for any natural specimen, *objet d'art*, curiosity or treatise which might conceivably contribute to an understanding of 'man and the natural world'. Horace Walpole, one of the trustees charged with looking after Sloane's collection following his death, described how he now spent most of his time 'in the guardianship of embryos and cockle-shells'. Sloane, he noted wryly, 'valued his collection at fourscore thousand [pounds]; and so would anybody who loves hippopotamuses, sharkes

with one ear, and spiders as big as geese! It is a rent-charge to keep the foetuses in spirit!'.

There was at first little attempt to bring any order to this impossible mishmash. The entrance hall of the original British Museum presented the visitor with a baffling array of Oriental idols, marble busts, elephants, sea-sponges, polar bears, portraits, fossils, meteorites, and a statue of Shakespeare, all topped off at the head of the staircase by several stuffed giraffes. Such a smorgasbord of the old, the beautiful, the exotic and the downright strange was very much a child of its time — a worthy ideal, but one that soon put great pressure on the Museum's limited human and material resources. Almost from the start, the great dilemma of the 'old curiosity shop in Great Russell Street' has been to reconcile its universalist aims with the practicalities of good housekeeping.

Antiquities formed only a small proportion of the foundation collections. Most of Sloane's exhibits related to the natural sciences and 'primitive' cultures. Even more numerous were his books, some 40 000 volumes. And the shelves were swelled still further by the addition of two other major private collections of manuscripts, the Cottonian Library (bequeathed to the nation in 1700) and the Harleian Manuscripts, purchased in 1753 with the remaining proceeds of the British Museum lottery. Four years later, the enormous Old Royal Library of the Kings of England was donated by George II. It is hardly surprising, then, that two of the original three departments of the Museum were devoted to this written material: a Department of Printed Books (including prints) and another of Manuscripts (including drawings and coins). The few antiquities were placed, along with all scientific and natural history specimens, ethnographic material and general curios, in a Department of Natural and Artificial Productions.

The growth of the antiquities collections in the early years was due largely to the many avid private collectors of the day, a number of whom endowed the Museum in their wills or left estates from which im-

portant pieces were purchased. During the later eighteenth and nineteenth centuries, Greece and Italy became firmly established on the itinerary of the Grand Tour, which well-born young men would take to acquaint themselves with Continental culture. Interest in the Classical arts was at its peak, and English noblemen soon began to collect antiquities and other works of art on their travels, especially in Italy, which was for a long time the main source of Classical artefacts. Excavations conducted by dealers, especially in Rome, Tivoli (the site of the emperor Hadrian's villa) and southern Italy, provided unrivalled opportunities for acquiring quantities of foreign relics. Many of the finest fruits of these labours eventually came to the Museum: the Hollis Collection in 1757, the Hamilton vases in 1772 and — the jewel in the crown — the Townley marbles in 1805. Displayed in his own home, Townley's superb collection of Classical sculptures — a number of which are included in this exhibition (cat. nos 68, 69, 71, 82, 83, 86, 90) — became a Mecca for the rich and famous of London during the late eighteenth century, and was justly regarded as one of the finest selections of its day anywhere in Europe.

Even this, however, was soon overshadowed by those most famous of all Classical sculptures, the Elgin marbles (so named after the seventh Earl of Elgin, who removed them from the Parthenon in Athens), commissioned by Pericles in the full flush of Athens's golden age. After

Charles Townley (seated right) in an idealized setting of his collection at his home in Park Street, London. With him are shown the French theorist Pierre Francois Huges (Baron d'Hancarville), and Townley's friends Charles Greville and Thomas Astle (standing). The *Discus Thrower* was added later. Painting by Johan Zoffany (1753–1810), 102.7 x 99.0 cm. (Bridgeman Art Library)

13

much wrangling over the price (eventually agreed at a miserly £35 000), these sculptures were purchased for the British Museum in 1816 and promptly installed to rapturous, if not yet universal, acclaim. 'De Greeks were Godes! De Greeks were Godes!', exclaimed the artist Henry Fuseli when he saw them, a sentiment shared by many. This acquisition set the seal on the Museum's transformation from a great library and natural history museum into a major artistic and archaeological showpiece, establishing it forever as a primary source for the study of the Classical past.

Interest in Egypt and the Middle East was slower to develop, the trustees of the Museum long maintaining that nothing produced in the Oriental kingdoms deserved to be exhibited alongside the sublime creations of the Greeks. Aside from a few mummies — already among the most popular exhibits — the Museum had very little to show from Egypt until 1802, when the antiquities confiscated as spoils of war from Napoleon's forces in Egypt arrived in London. The great prize of this haul was the Rosetta Stone, a trilingual inscription which eventually provided the key to the decipherment of Egyptian hieroglyphic writing (a feat achieved, to British chagrin, by a Frenchman!). A few years later the British Consul-General in Egypt, Henry Salt, and the Swiss traveller J.-L. Burckhardt presented the Museum with a colossal bust of Ramesses II, earlier described by a connoisseur as 'the most beautiful and perfect piece of sculpture that can be seen throughout the whole country (of Egypt)'. Weighing many tonnes, its removal was a major engineering feat (Napoleon's expedition had earlier tried to move it and failed) for which Salt engaged the advice of an Italian theatrical strongman and adventurer, Giovanni Belzoni. Encouraged by the interest the bust aroused in London, Salt and Belzoni set about acquiring more monumental sculptures for the Museum. Between 1817 and 1819 they managed to secure some of the largest figures ever removed from Egypt, including a number of statues from the mortuary temple of

Amenophis III at Thebes (Luxor). These overpowering works did much to convey the grandeur of Egyptian civilization and remain today among the most striking exhibits of the Egyptian galleries.

As the nineteenth century progressed, the Museum began to play a more active and responsible role in the unearthing of antiquities, inspiring or sponsoring archaeological excavations of its own. The 'scramble for antiquities' was often scandalously unscientific by modern standards; many early digs were little more than treasure hunts. But the gradual emergence of more rigorous excavation and recording techniques eventually allowed objects to be assigned a stratigraphical context from which their historical and cultural importance could begin to be understood.

Classical Greek art remained the primary focus of interest. A number of expeditions were sent to western Turkey, which had fallen within the Greek cultural orbit for much of antiquity, and where many spectacular funerary monuments and temples lay partly exposed to view. Among the prizes brought back were remains of two of the 'Seven Wonders of the Ancient World': the massive tomb of King Maussolos from Halicarnassus (excavated 1856–57, 1865) and the Temple of Artemis at Ephesus (1869–74).

Most of the Middle East, meanwhile, remained *terra incognita*. Until mid-century the lands east of Egypt and Syria–Palestine saw no serious archaeological work and were visited only by a handful of the most intrepid travellers. The Museum, therefore, had virtually nothing to represent the great empires of Assyria, Babylonia and Persia other than a few inscribed mud-bricks, carved boundary stones and some fragments of Persian relief sculptures.

This situation changed dramatically in 1845 when Henry Layard began digging in the ruins of the ancient capitals of Assyria. In the royal palaces of Nimrud and Nineveh, Layard (and in later years his assistant Rassam) unearthed room after room lined with carved stone reliefs of fabulous demons and deities (cat. no. 7), scenes of battles, royal hunts (cat. no. 8) and ceremonies;

doorways flanked by enormous winged bulls and lions; and, inside some of the chambers, thousands of inscribed clay tablets in the curious, and at that time undeciphered, cuneiform script (cat. no. 12). The Museum sponsored Layard's work, and many of the best reliefs and other finds were shipped back to England. The nineteenth-century fascination with the Bible assured these illustrations of Old Testament history an excited reception. The sculptures proved a great attraction, drawing large crowds whenever a new shipment was displayed. Layard's discoveries had captured the public imagination and his account of their recovery, *Nineveh and Its Remains*, soon took the country by storm.

By the beginning of the twentieth century, the antiquities departments covering the early centres of Old World civilization had assumed something like their present form. Important acquisitions continued to be made, but only Leonard Woolley's excavations at Ur 'of the Chaldees' in ancient Sumer (southern Iraq) opened up completely new and unexpected vistas, revealing for the

One of the winged bulls which guarded the entrances to King Ashurnasirpal II's palace at Nimrud, being hauled up the steps of the British Museum. (*Illustrated London News*, Feb. 28, 1852)

first time the true wealth and sophistication in early Sumerian civilization. Woolley's aims in the 1920s show how much things had changed from the days of Layard: 'Our object', he declared, 'was to get history, not to fill museum cases with miscellaneous curios'. Yet miscellaneous curios there were, and in abundance, especially in the so-called Royal Tombs. Many splendid statues, inlays, tools, harps and lyres of gold, lapis lazuli and other precious materials from these marvellous burials came to the Museum in recognition of its support for Woolley's work (cat. nos 4,5).

The growth of the Museum during its 230-year existence made Sloane's original universalist ideal increasingly impracticable. Montagu House was soon bursting at the seams and had to be demolished to make way for the present more commodious buildings, erected between 1823 and 1852. Even these, however, proved inadequate, and various parts of the collections were successively hived off, forming the basis for a number of independent institutions. Chief among these secondary foundations was the British Museum (Natural History) in South Kensington (1881). Old Master paintings originally destined for the Museum became instead the inspiration for a National Gallery (1824), which in turn spawned the National Portrait Gallery (1856) and the Tate Gallery (1897). The ethnographic collections have since 1970 been exhibited in a separate building in Piccadilly known as the Museum of Mankind, but this material will return to Bloomsbury before the end of the century. Most recently, the Library departments, the very core of the original foundation, were separated in 1973 to form the basis of a new British Library, a national archive designed to meet the needs of the twenty-first century. After much debate, however, the issue of whether the historic collections of the old library departments will move to their new home near King's Cross still hangs in the balance.

Despite these divestments, the British Museum retains to this day a tangible legacy of Sloane's all-embracing eclecticism. In addition to the antiquities from Europe and the Middle East, for which it is now most famous, there still exist, side by side under the one roof, departments of Prints and Drawings, Coins and Medals, Oriental Antiquities, and Medieval and Later Antiquities, all of which count among their collections objects made as recently as this century. Sloane would be pleased to see that, along with the relics of the grand civilizations and exotic cultures, there is still a place for a 1934 German coffee pot. And the Ethnography Department casts its net wider still, drawing from pre-industrial societies the world over.

The Museum has diversified, too, in function if not scope. The 'old curiosity shop' has met the challenge of the twentieth century by greatly expanding its educational role and by establishing, in 1923, a laboratory for conservation that has been at the forefront of modern research into ancient technology. First and foremost, the British Museum remains, as it has long been, one of the finest collections of antiquities in the world — a rare 'temple of the arts' where one can study civilization in the round.

The British Museum, c.1860. Constructed between 1823 and 1852, the building's Greek Revival facade reflected the contemporary enthusiasm for Classical Greece.
(British Museum)

Catalogue

The works in each section of this catalogue have been arranged in chronological order except in instances where their style or characteristics place them more logically within an alternative framework. Small objects — coins, gems, jewellery and figurines — of different dates have therefore been grouped together, and Roman copies of Greek works have been arranged according to the date of the Greek original.

Caption information includes the title and/or description of the work, followed by date of manufacture, place of discovery, medium and measurements and/or weights. Measurements are given in centimetres or metres, height before width before depth unless otherwise specified, and weights are given in grams.

Civilization

The men and women who inhabited the earth 10 000 years ago were physically almost identical to ourselves. Scrubbed down and dressed in modern clothes, a group of late Stone-Age hunter-gatherers walking down the street today probably would not turn any heads. And yet their lifestyles, their relations with one another and with the world around them, the thoughts they carried in their heads — all this and much else sets our distant forebears unequivocally apart.

The difference, in a word, is civilization — or rather civilizations. For, from continent to continent and region to region, civilization arose in many different ways and took many different forms. General benchmarks which apply equally to China and Greece or to Mexico and Egypt are difficult to set: many early civilizations invented or adopted some form of writing, but others did not; some technically advanced peoples did not use the wheel; a few remained ignorant of metals; and so on. But definitions and touchstones are less important than the clear fact of the enormous differences between then and now. The word 'civilization' conveniently captures — though it certainly does not explain — the changes that have taken place.

One basic prerequisite of all urban civilization was the ability to produce enough food to free some of the community from tilling the fields, allowing them to devote time to other pursuits. In the great riverine civilizations of Mesopotamia, Egypt and China, this breakthrough came with the advent of sophisticated irrigation farming. Higher crop yields supported much greater concentrations of population, and thus were born the first towns and, eventually, cities.

It was this urban revolution that the Australian archaeologist V. Gordon Childe (1892–1957) — generally regarded as the greatest prehistorian of the century — saw as the crucial watershed. Itself the first outcome of the urbanization process, the town was also the focus around which other manifestations of civilization appeared — monumental architecture, burgeoning arts and crafts, new bureaucratic institutions and inventions such as writing.

In Childe's day, Mesopotamia was regarded as the cradle of 'Old World' civilization, and the appearance of other technologically advanced societies from Europe to China was believed to be traceable ultimately to this source. This diffusionist picture has since proved too simple. As was certainly the case in the 'New World' of the Americas, so too in Europe and Asia other 'advanced' and urban cultures seem to have arisen through essentially internal processes of change.

But the Near East and Egypt retain the special interest of having been first on a number of important counts. As far as we know today, the earliest urban, literate civilizations arose along the banks of the Tigris–Euphrates and Nile rivers. And at least in the Near Eastern context, their example accelerated the emergence of other urban cultures.

The more immediate roots of Western civilization, however, lie further west in the Classical cultures that succeeded the empires of the Near East as the focus of political power and cultural innovation during the first millennium BC. The achievements of the Greeks, transmitted through the Romans and the Renaissance to modern times, played a uniquely influential role in shaping the arts, institutions and thinking of the Western world. Australia is about as far from Greece as it is possible to be, and yet diverse aspects of everyday life, from the columned façades of our banks to the name and principles of our democratic constitution, are testimony to the enduring legacy of the Classical past.

The character and individuality of a civilization may be manifested in many different ways — in its religion, literature or government no less than in its visual arts. It is these arts, however, which lose their impact least as time and culture move on, remaining vivid and accessible when much else of a people's distinctive achievement begins to seem distant and unintelligible. Presenting a selection of works of art from some of the major cultures of the Middle East and the Classical world, **Civilization** brings us into direct contact with the creative talents of the peoples who contributed most to the genesis of Western civilization — and through the images they created provides an insight into their conceptions of themselves and the world around them.

The Ancient World

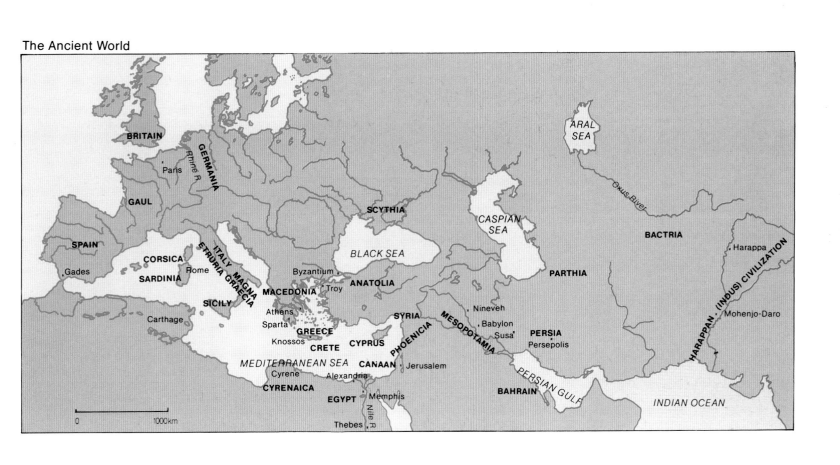

BRITAIN

GERMANIA

Paris · Rhine R.

GAUL

SPAIN

· Gades

CORSICA

SARDINIA

ITALY ETRURIA MAGNA GRAECIA

· Rome

Carthage

SICILY

SCYTHIA

BLACK SEA

Byzantium ·

MACEDONIA

· Troy

ANATOLIA

Athens ·

Sparta

GREECE

Knossos ·

CRETE

CYPRUS

MEDITERRANEAN SEA

CYRENAICA

Cyrene ·

· Alexandria

CANAAN

· Jerusalem

EGYPT

· Memphis

Nile R.

Thebes ·

SYRIA

PHOENICIA

ARAL SEA

CASPIAN SEA

BACTRIA

Oxus River

PARTHIA

· Harappa

MESOPOTAMIA

· Nineveh

· Babylon

Susa ·

PERSIA

· Persepolis

BAHRAIN

PERSIAN GULF

HARAPPAN (INDUS) CIVILIZATION

· Mohenjo-Daro

INDIAN OCEAN

0   1000km

The Cradle of Civilization: The Near East

When Alexander the Great led the Macedonian army into Mesopotamia in 331 BC, the beginnings of recorded history in the world he was entering were already more remote from him than the birth of Christ is from us today. The prospect of coming face to face with civilizations incomparably older than his own no doubt enhanced the allure of the East, to which Alexander was drawn by his mission of conquering the Persians, who had invaded Greece and put Athens to the torch a century and a half earlier. For, despite their disdain of Oriental despotism, the Greeks had always been intrigued by the Near East — by the imponderable antiquity of its monuments, the esoteric wisdom of its priests, and the sumptuous splendour of its court life. Over 2000 years later, it is still the fascination of cultures at once so ancient, so grand and so exotic that gives the region its unique interest. As far as we know today, it is here that the story of civilization begins.

The ancient Near East — corresponding approximately to what is today called the Middle East — lay at the crossroads of Europe, Asia and Africa. Stretching from Anatolia and Palestine to the far reaches of Iran, this vast and geographically varied region comprised many different landscapes and a multitude of peoples whose destinies were drawn together as much by the vicissitudes of history as by any common culture.

As today, ancient Mesopotamia (Iraq) and her western neighbours — Syria, Lebanon and Palestine — were dominated by Semites: the Akkadians, Babylonians and Assyrians in Mesopotamia; the Syrian-based Amorites and Arameans; and the Phoenicians, Canaanites and Hebrews in the Levant. Around this 'fertile crescent' of plains and foothills, the wild highlands of Anatolia and Iran supported a host of non-Semitic peoples. Some of these, like the Hittites, Scythians and Persians, spoke Indo-European languages, the broad family to which English also belongs; others, like the Urartians, Kassites and Elamites, spoke tongues with no known affiliations. The Sumerians, the first linguistically identifiable inhabitants of southern Mesopotamia, also fall into this enigmatic category.

The first urban literate society — arguably the first civilization in human history — arose in the centuries before 3000 BC in the flat mud-plains of Sumer (southern Mesopotamia). As in Egypt, where similar processes can be traced back almost as far, the economic foundation of this epochal development was irrigation agriculture, based here on the twin rivers that gave Mesopotamia its Greek name — literally '(the land) between the rivers'. The much greater harvests made possible by controlling the annual floodwaters of the Tigris and Euphrates supported a vastly more concentrated population and provided a surplus which could be traded for metals and other foreign raw materials.

By about 3300 BC the town of Uruk (biblical Erech) had far surpassed all other Sumerian settlements in size and importance. A major walled town of some 100 hectares, housing more than 10 000 people, it was in its day the largest concentration of people anywhere in the world. The key social and political aspects of Uruk's rise to pre-eminence remain elusive, but archaeology reveals the physical manifestations of the great changes that were taking place. The appearance of monumental architecture (one of Uruk's early temples covers over twice the area of the Parthenon in Athens); explosive advances in sculpture and other arts; the invention of the first known system of writing (cat. no.1) — indeed, in almost every walk of life the Uruk Period marks a crucial turning point.

An outline of historical events begins to emerge from Sumerian royal inscriptions around 2700 BC. Earlier generations of rulers are the subjects of epic poems, among them Gilgamesh of Uruk, whose quest for eternal life (cat. no.12) has lost none of its poignancy through the centuries. How much of the more historical-sounding tales reflect real events is impossible to say. A vivid picture of the splendour of court life and burial around this time is provided by the Royal Tombs of Ur (cat. nos 4, 5).

Mesopotamian history is dominated by the rise and fall of great empires, interspersed with invasions and periods of anarchy. Most kingdoms eventually fell to foreigners, usually highlanders eager to plunder the rich cities of the plains. Some of these intruders made swift, devastating razzias and returned home; but others — notably the Amorites, Kassites and Arameans — settled down and were absorbed into Mesopotamian society. Thus, out of the ashes of the fallen regime a new order would emerge, invigorated by the influx of new peoples, ideas and loyalties. Indeed, most of Mesopotamia's greatest rulers were born of these new arrivals: Sargon of Agade was an Akkadian, Hammurabi an Amorite, and Nebuchadnezzar an Aramean (Chaldean).

The focus of Mesopotamian political power vacillated between the north and south of the land, and despite their largely shared culture, a rivalry, at times breaking into open hostility, always remained between the two regions. In the north, along the Tigris, lay the grassy steppes of Assyria, the homeland of the mighty warriors of the first millennium BC. Babylonia, the flat floodplain south of modern Baghdad, incorporated the ancient land of Sumer, whose cultural and historical pre-eminence was acknowledged by all.

The first great Mesopotamian empire, and the one against which all later kings would measure their achievement, was forged by Sargon of Agade (c.2371–2316 BC), whose rise to power also represented the political coming of age of the Akkadians. Welding the Sumerian city-states into a single kingdom centred on his capital at Agade (still undiscovered), Sargon launched a series of bold campaigns east and west, conquering all the lands from the 'Upper' to the 'Lower' Sea (the Mediterranean coast of Syria to the head of the Persian Gulf) and taunted posterity with the challenge: 'Any king who would call himself my equal, wherever I went, there let him go!'.

The collapse of the Akkadian Empire was followed by a short-lived Sumerian revival under the leadership of the Third

The Near East

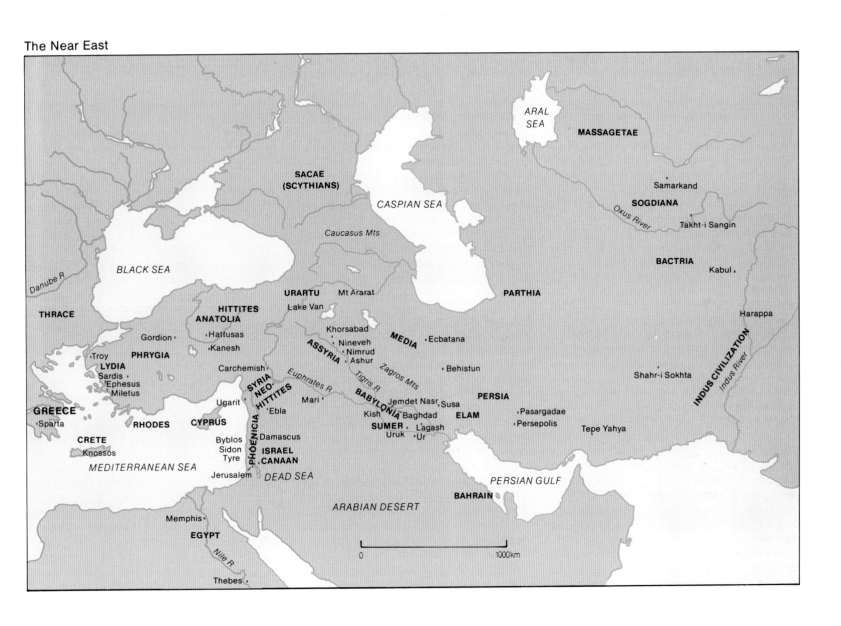

THRACE

BLACK SEA

Danube R

SACAE
(SCYTHIANS)

CASPIAN SEA

Caucasus Mts

ARAL
SEA

MASSAGETAE

Samarkand

SOGDIANA

Oxus River

Takht-i Sangin

BACTRIA

Kabul

PARTHIA

URARTU   Mt Ararat
Lake Van

HITTITES
ANATOLIA

Gordion

Hattusas
Kanesh

PHRYGIA

Troy

LYDIA
Sardis
Ephesus
Miletus

Carchemish

Khorsabad

Nineveh
Nimrud
Ashur

ASSYRIA

Euphrates R

SYRIA
NEO-
HITTITES

Ugarit

Ebla   Mari

Tigris R

Zagros Mts

MEDIA

Ecbatana

Behistun

Harappa

INDUS CIVILIZATION

Indus River

Shahr-i Sokhta

BABYLONIA

Jemdet Nasr
Kish   Susa
Baghdad
SUMER   Lagash
Uruk   Ur

PERSIA

ELAM

Pasargadae
Persepolis

Tepe Yahya

GREECE

Sparta

RHODES   CYPRUS

CRETE
Knossos

MEDITERRANEAN SEA

PHOENICIA

Byblos
Sidon
Tyre

Damascus

ISRAEL
CANAAN

Jerusalem   DEAD SEA

PERSIAN GULF

BAHRAIN

ARABIAN DESERT

Memphis

EGYPT

Nile R

Thebes

0   1000km

Dynasty of Ur. This proved to be the swan-song of these extraordinary people; the Sumerians disappear as a recognizable group after about 2000 BC as their descendants adopted the Babylonian (Akkadian) language. But Sumerian remained the scribal language of priests and scholars for another 2000 years, and the legacy of their culture continued to be felt in almost every aspect of Mesopotamian life.

Few kings in later centuries managed to control Iran beyond the mid-ranges of the Zagros Mountains, where they were held at bay by the hostile forces of Elam and fierce semi-nomadic tribes. The general pattern of Mesopotamian expansion was rather to follow the Akkadian kings' conquests into Syria, whence the ambitious Neo-Assyrian and Neo-Babylonian conquerors of the first millennium BC would march south through Palestine and into Egypt, bringing all the biblical lands of the Levant under their sway. The highland kingdom of Urartu around Lake Van proved more resistant, and this northern neighbour long remained a deep thorn in Assyria's side.

Until the sixth century BC, the kings of Mesopotamia's great empires, even if descended from foreign stock, had ruled from capitals within the Tigris–Euphrates valley. Thus when Cyrus the Great overthrew the last Neo-Babylonian king in 539 BC and absorbed Mesopotamia into the burgeoning Persian (Achaemenid) Empire, native pride was struck a wounding blow. The material culture of the Persians owed much to Mesopotamia, but language, religion and customs set these Indo-Aryans apart. They proved tolerant overlords, however, respecting the local customs of their subjects. King Cyrus is still remembered by the Jews for allowing the Babylonian exiles to return to Jerusalem.

At its height, the Persian Empire extended from the Indo-Iranian borderlands to Egypt, far eclipsing even the greatest Mesopotamian kingdoms. But, after only two centuries, this too was swept away in the whirlwind campaigns of Alexander the Great (334–323 BC), which turned the tables and for the first time saw Europe become master

of the East. The succeeding Hellenistic and Roman Periods represent a foreign interlude when the native culture was overlaid by a Mediterranean veneer. Mesopotamia passed from Greek (Seleucid) control to the Iranian-based Parthians in the second century BC. The return to the Oriental fold was firmly and decisively confirmed by the coming of Islam in the seventh century AD, when the followers of the prophet Muhammed rode out of Arabia and set the Near East alight with the fervour of their belief. This was in many ways a new beginning and — like the Christianization of the Roman Empire in the West — represents a convenient point to mark the end of antiquity in the Near East.

Religion suffused private and public life in Mesopotamia to an extent that is difficult to comprehend from a modern Western viewpoint. The numerous gods and goddesses of the Mesopotamian pantheon, each personifying some concept, skill or natural phenomenon, were believed to determine man's destiny in a very direct and personal way. Any event, from the successful completion of a business deal to the fall of a great empire, might be attributed to the intervention of the gods, imagined to be fully as fickle and partisan as humans. Elaborate methods were therefore contrived to determine their will by examining omens, either unsolicited signs such as unusual animal behaviour and dreams, or by deliberately testing the pattern of oil on water, the shape and colour of sacrificial animals' entrails, and so on. For this last practice, model livers in clay were inscribed with the names of their various parts and what they indicated. 'If the finger of the liver is like a cow's tongue', a typical entry reads, 'his eunuchs will murder the king'. No temple would be founded or war waged without obtaining a favourable omen from the relevant god.

Most cultic activities were conducted by priests behind closed doors, the public participating only in major festivals. The temples were imposing buildings, often set on a raised platform and lavishly decorated with precious metals and stones. The famous

ziggurats, including the Bible's 'Tower of Babel', were essentially more massive staged podiums, with staircases leading to a small shrine at the top. The cult statue of the god in the inner sanctum of the temple was clothed and fed daily, the food later being consumed by the priests. The temples of major deities supported large priesthoods which managed these gods' often considerable estates. The temple was an economic as well as a religious institution, engaging in agriculture, manufacturing and trade, and would expect to receive booty and slaves from a successful campaign by the king. Priests were the scholars of their day and education took place in temple schools.

The patron gods of the great capitals became also the state deities of the empires — Ashur for Assyria, Marduk for Babylonia. A variable core of eight or so other major deities was worshipped throughout Mesopotamia (cat. no. 6), while numerous lesser gods had local followings. There was, in addition, a multitude of demons, represented with animals' heads or as hybrid monsters, which brought sickness and ill-fortune and had to be kept at bay or, if necessary, exorcised with spells by the incantation priest.

Many of the early rulers of Sumer bore priestly titles, and even later, when church and state were largely distinct, the king was regarded as the city-god's deputy on earth, his 'chosen one' who would act as high-priest on important religious occasions. The king was also the fountainhead of justice, whose duty it was to see 'that justice shine forth in the land, that the evil and dishonest be confounded, and that the strong not oppress the weak', as Hammurabi proclaims in his famous law code.

The subjects of Mesopotamian art reflect its two principal sources of patronage — the temple and the palace. Deities and scenes of worship are complemented by representations of the king valiantly triumphing over his enemies, hunting or celebrating a victory. Themes can be traced and novelties identified through the centuries, but there is little natural logic to the order of styles beyond the passing down from one period to the next of a repertory of subjects and motifs. Assyrian and Persian kings are shown galloping along in their chariots much like the Sumerians 2000 years earlier (cat. nos 5, 8, 15), but the rendering of the dumpy Sumerian figures is worlds apart from their Assyrian descendants, in which the superficial anatomy of limbs and joints is widely exploited as a rich source of decorative effects.

Elegance, clarity of design and sheer craftsmanship reached new heights under the Persians, who adapted the Near Eastern repertoire of motifs — and others of their own — drawing on the great talent of the northern steppe artists for decoratively stylizing natural forms (cat. nos 14–16). Other influences from as far as Greece may be detected in their work, which concentrates particularly on images of real and mythical animals, but these were welded together in new and distinctive ways.

The nearer Eastern lands fronting onto the Mediterranean also played tutor to the Greco-Roman world at certain crucial times. The Greeks copied their alphabet — which was later adapted by the Romans and passed on to us — from the Phoenicians, the same people whose exotic traded handiworks infused Greek art of the Orientalizing Period with the new spirit, motifs and themes that set in motion the extraordinary artistic developments of the Archaic and Classical Periods. And in Roman times, it was in Palestine, on the western fringe of the Near East, that a new religion was born which was to win the heart and soul of Rome, and through the Byzantine Empire came to dominate the Western world.

The Near Eastern legacy to Western civilization is easily underestimated, for it has been transmitted to us through the Greeks and Romans, who selected, adapted and gave a new character to much of what they passed on. A handful of words, including 'alcohol' (Akkadian *guhlu*) and 'cane' (*qanu*); the sexagesimal division of our compasses and watches; the positional system of numeration; and the Tree-of-Life motif in art — such are the scant vestiges of Mesopotamian culture directly recognizable in our lives today.

But the Mesopotamian impact on the Greeks, and through them on the future development of Western civilization, ran much deeper. Greek mathematics, astronomy and medicine were all greatly indebted to the Babylonians, who had calculated the value of π (pi) to five decimal places and the duration of the solar year to within four and a half minutes. Able to predict eclipses and other celestial events with great accuracy, it is little wonder that the 'Chaldean seers' left such a deep impression on the authors of the Old Testament.

Early writing from Sumer and Egypt

Sumerian ration list
3200–2900 BC (Uruk III Period)
Sumer (southern Iraq); probably inscribed at
Jemdet Nasr or Uruk
clay
7.8 x 7.8 cm

cat. no. 1

Egyptian hieroglyphic inscription of King Den
*c.*3000 BC (1st Dynasty)
Abydos, Egypt
ivory
4.5 x 5.4 cm

cat. no. 2

Sumerian list of fields and their yields in barley
2039 BC, Year 8 of King Amar-sin (3rd Dynasty
of Ur)
Sumer (southern Iraq); probably inscribed
at Lagash
clay
10.7 cm diameter

cat. no. 3

> The scribal art is the mother of orators (and) the father of scholars;
> The scribal art is delightful, it never satiates you;
> The scribal art is not (easily) learnt, (but) he who has learned it need no longer be anxious about it;
> Strive to (master) the scribal art and it will enrich you;
> Be industrious in the scribal art and it will provide you with wealth and abundance.

Thus a Sumerian poem, preserved on clay tablets dating to about 1800 BC, sums up the delights and rewards of writing. The scribe who copied it — and no doubt the anonymous author — was himself a Sumerian, one of the short, dark-haired people who are the first identifiable inhabitants of southern Mesopotamia (Iraq). The 'scribal art' which he practised and praised was in his day already some 1500 years old, and he had every reason to be proud of this long and fruitful tradition — for it was his forebears who had begun it all.

The oldest writing yet discovered anywhere in the world comes from the Sumerian city of Uruk, biblical Erech, and dates to about 3400 BC. Incised on clay (rarely stone) tablets, it records the Sumerians' unusual language, which is unrelated to any other known tongue. Egyptian hieroglyphic writing (cat. no. 2) seems to have been invented somewhat later, around 3000 BC, and there is reason to believe that the idea — though not the form of the script — was inspired by the Sumerian example.

Between them, these two very different scripts seem to have stimulated the invention of all the other forms of writing which subsequently appeared in the ancient Near East and Europe. For independent scripts which were not inspired by these systems, we have to look far afield to China and the Americas, and even in these regions writing did not begin until many centuries later — Chinese characters in about 1500 BC, and Olmec hieroglyphs in Central America some time after 1000 BC.

The early Sumerian tablet (cat. no. 1), dating to about 3200 BC, is a list of rations issued by the priestly administration during the course of five days. Each day's rations are on a separate line, with the days indicated at the left by the sign for 'day' (⌣) — a picture of the sun appearing over the horizon — together with the appropriate number of impressed digits (⌓) from one to five. The numbers at the right record the amounts of various commodities issued on that day, (using digits turned ninety degrees from the others and including ○ for 'ten'). Running down the ends of the lines we see that the last entries record five, five, five, fifteen and ten units of an agricultural commodity (its precise identity is unknown) represented by the sign △. The groups of more complex linear signs between the ration and day numbers are names, probably those of the supervising officials or the recipients.

The third inscription (cat. no. 3) shows how the Sumerian script developed during the next thousand years. It is a list of the yields in barley from a series of fields, and dates to the end of the third millennium BC, the last period when Sumerian was used as an everyday language. (After 2000 BC, like Latin in medieval Europe, Sumerian was learnt only by scholars.) The Sumerians of this period, the so-called Third Dynasty of Ur, took bureaucratic accounting to un-precedented extremes. Everything was written down in exact and painstaking detail: every stage of agricultural production, all the rations distributed to labourers and messengers, the artefacts produced by workshops, and so on. Thanks to this bureaucratic explosion, more texts have been recovered from the twenty-first century BC than from any other period of Mesopotamian history — tens of thousands of tablets, many of which still lie in museum basements waiting to be read.

The early Egyptian hieroglyphic text (cat. no. 2) is from the tomb of Den, a king of the First Dynasty, around 3000 BC. Most early Egyptian writing relates to the king and his court, and this plaque is a label for a pair of Den's sandals, as indicated by the drawing scratched on the back. The front of the label bears a picture of the king beating a kneeling enemy with a mace, explained by the inscription at far right: 'Year of the First Time of Smiting the East(erners)' — that is, the inhabitants of Palestine or the desert east of the Nile. Three signs under the king's left arm proclaim: 'they [the enemy] shall not exist'. The smiting gesture was to become the classic symbol of the conquering pharaoh, repeated countless times on royal monuments for thousands of years. The king's name (indicated by a hand and a wavy line) is placed before his face in a rectangular frame (*serekh*) surmounted by the falcon of the god Horus. The pole on the right bears the emblem of the jackal-god Wepwawet ('the Opener of the Ways'), one of four such standards associated with the king in early times.

The invention of writing in Sumer represents perhaps the greatest single milestone in the emergence of civilization. The ability to record information in a retrievable form greatly facilitated the administration of agriculture, animal husbandry, public works and other communal activities essential to urban life in Mesopotamia. The earliest writing was clearly a bureaucratic aid devised to meet these mundane needs. But it was not long before the versatility of the new invention was realized and writing was put to other uses — first for various lexical lists of objects by categories and eventually for a wide range of literary genres, from letters and royal decrees to myths and omens — becoming in time the vehicle of Mesopotamian culture itself.

The earliest texts from Uruk, dating to about 3400 BC, were found among the ruins of two large temple precincts. The priesthood clearly played a key role in agricultural and economic organization, and these early accounts record disbursements, receipts and inventories of sheep, grain and other commodities under their control. The earliest texts are written with pictographic signs (stylized drawings of objects), many of which can be interpreted, though it is often not possible to read them phonetically. Direct evidence for the pronunciation of the signs begins only in the succeeding period (3200–2900 BC), to which the ration list tablet is dated, when the occasional addition of grammatical endings to the words confirms that the language being recorded is Sumerian. By this stage the rounded pictographs had been reduced to more abstract shapes based on straight lines, rendered by impressing a cut reed into the moist clay. Thus were created the distinctive cuneiform ('wedge-shaped') characters which, gradually simplified and refined, were to serve as the basis of Mesopotamian writing throughout antiquity. The 'day' sign at the left of the lines (◁▷) is still recognizable as a drawing of the rising sun. In its more developed cuneiform shape (turned upwards ninety degrees), it appears purely geometric (◇). Essentially the same script was adopted by many other Near Eastern peoples to write their own languages: Akkadian (Assyrian and Babylonian) in Mesopotamia, Eblaite in Syria, Hittite, Hurrian and Urartian in Anatolia, and Elamite in Iran. Other cuneiform scripts were devised for Ugaritic in Syria, and for Proto-Elamite and Old Persian in Iran. By AD 70, when the last known Akkadian document was inscribed, the cuneiform tradition had lasted some 3500 years.

Egyptian hieroglyphic writing, unlike Mesopotamian cuneiform, never lost its pictorial character. The signs were more faithful images to begin with, and they remained recognizable drawings for more than 3000 years — indeed, the latest hieroglyphs of Roman times are among the most detailed pictures. In Den's inscription we can easily identify a fish, feather, and pair of raised arms in the inscription at left (probably an official's name); a hand forming part of the king's name (Den); and a dagger at the right. Like cuneiform, many signs represent whole words, but from very early times the Egyptian scribes also used hieroglyphs which stood for a single letter. It was probably this practice that stimulated the creation of the first pure alphabet in Syro-Palestine in the second millennium BC, an invention from which all later alphabets, including our own, ultimately derive. For everyday use the Egyptians also created a cursive (running-writing) version of the hieroglyphs (called 'hieratic') in which the pictures are reduced to quickly sketchable abstract signs.

The development of selected cuneiform signs. The cuneiform ('wedge-shaped') script of Mesopotamia rapidly evolved from simple drawings ('pictograms') of objects into more abstract signs. Egyptian hieroglyphs, by contrast, always remained recognizable pictures. (British Museum)

cat. no. 1   cat. no. 3

cat. no. 2

27

Sumerian vessels

c.2600 BC (Early Dynastic III Period)
from the tomb of Queen Pu-abi at Ur, Sumer
(southern Iraq)
gold
spouted bowl 12.4 x 17.5 cm;
oval bowl 7.0 x 19.7 cm diameter
cat. no. 4

The Royal Cemetery at the Sumerian city of Ur is the 'Tutankhamun's Tomb' of Mesopotamian archaeology. Only a few years after that greatest of all modern discoveries, Sir Leonard Woolley's excavations in the 1920s at Ur 'of the Chaldees' — familiar from the Bible as the traditional home of Abraham — revealed to a spellbound public the extraordinary richness and sophistication of early Sumerian civilization. Here was gold and treasure on a scale never before encountered in the Near East, and at a date more than a thousand years before 'King Tut'. With an 'unbeatable combination of the Bible, human sacrifice and gold' it is little wonder that the great Ur Exhibition at the British Museum in 1928 attracted record crowds.

These gold vessels are two of eight found in the tomb of the Sumerian queen Pu-abi. Her burial was one of only two 'royal' tombs which were discovered unrobbed, and the only one whose owner can be identified with certainty (the names of other 'queens' and 'kings' are inscribed on certain objects but their tombs cannot now be identified). Her name (earlier misread 'Shub-ad'), with the title queen (nin), is inscribed on the lapis lazuli cylinder seal which she wore pinned to the right arm of her burial gown.

Each of the Royal Tombs consisted of a rectangular shaft approached by a sloping ramp. In one part of this great pit a vaulted burial chamber was constructed, the rest of the area being left for the attendants — up to seventy in number — whose unfortunate lot it was to follow their master or mistress into the other world. On the basis of the finds, Woolley vividly reconstructs the macabre ceremony in which they met their deaths.

Down into the open pit, with its mat-covered floor and mat-lined walls, empty and unfurnished, there comes a procession of people, the members of the dead ruler's court, soldiers and man-servants, and women, the latter in all their finery of brightly coloured garments and head-dresses of carnelian and lapis lazuli, silver and gold, officers with the insignia of their rank, musicians bearing harps or lyres, and then, driven or backed down the slope, the chariots drawn by the oxen, the drivers in the cars, and grooms holding the heads of the draught animals, and all take up their allotted places at the bottom of the shaft and finally a guard of soldiers forms up at the entrance. Each man and woman brought a little cup, ... the only equipment needed for the rite that was to follow. There would seem to have been some kind of a service down there, at least it is certain that the musicians played up to the last, then each of them drank from their cups a potion which they had brought with them or found prepared on the spot — in one case we found in the middle of the pit a great copper pot into which they could have dipped — and they lay down and composed themselves for death. Somebody came down and killed the animals and perhaps saw to it that all was decently in order ... and when that was done, earth was flung in from above, over the unconscious victims, and the filling-in of the grave-shaft was begun.

Pu-abi's death-pit contained twenty-six victims, including five armed guards, ten lavishly bejewelled ladies-in-waiting — one of them a harpist who died with her finger still on the strings of her instrument — and four grooms for the oxen which drew her ceremonial sledge-chariot. In the thickly-walled burial chamber was the queen, laid out on a wooden bier, accompanied by three personal maids. None of these attendants was provided with funerary goods, for they were there simply to serve their queen.

The funeral treasure, a total of over two hundred objects, comprised everything Pu-abi would need in the after-life: various kinds of vessels (some containing food and drink), drinking straws, a gaming board, a clothes chest, offering tables, tools and weapons as well as personal items of jewellery, elaborate head-dresses, cylinder seals, clothes, decorations and so on. Most of these are common enough types of objects, but they are exceptional for the precious materials from which even the supposedly utilitarian items were made, and for their fine craftsmanship and decoration. Wherever Woolley and his men turned the soil they found gold and silver, lapis lazuli, cornelian, agate and other precious substances, all of it carved, sculpted and inlaid in sumptuous works of splendid extravagance. A lyre was decorated with a bull's head of gold incorporating a lapis lazuli beard; vessels were fashioned from solid gold, silver, obsidian and even lapis lazuli, or ostrich egg-shells encrusted with mother-of-pearl. Sea-shells used as receptacles for eye-paint were reproduced for Pu-abi in gold and silver; and there was even a set of chisels and a saw, all made of solid gold.

It is the abundance of gold above all else that is so dazzling. Consumed with a quite unabashed conspicuousness, more gold has been recovered from the tombs at Ur than from all other excavations in Mesopotamia combined. The walls of the oval bowl displayed here, found with a silver drinking tube beside Pu-abi's head, are far thicker than they need be for any functional purpose. Weighing 445.5 grams, this is a work of pure extravagance. The other bowl, perhaps a feeding bottle, was one of four gold vessels found together in the death pit outside the burial chamber.

History unfortunately tells us nothing of Pu-abi or the other rulers buried in the tombs. They do not appear in the Sumerian King List and, though Woolley believed them to be kings and queens, others have suggested that they were priests and priestesses of the Sumerian moon-god Nanna, whose chief shrine was at Ur. The head of Nanna's cult was always a priestess, known as his 'wife' — a fact which might explain the high proportion of women in the 'royal' tombs.

cat. no. 4

The 'Standard of Ur'

Probably the sounding box of a Sumerian
musical instrument showing a war scene (front)
and a banquet (back)
*c.*2600 BC (Early Dynastic III Period)
from Royal Tomb 779 at Ur, Sumer (southern Iraq)
lapis lazuli, limestone and shell set in bitumen
21.6 x 50.5 x 11.5 cm
cat. no. 5

The treasure recovered by Sir Leonard
Woolley from the Royal Tombs at Ur represents only a portion of the riches originally
buried there. A number of the tombs had
been robbed, not by modern pillagers but by
the tomb builders themselves, who sometimes came upon old burials in the course of
cutting the shaft for a new chamber, and
could not always resist the temptation to
pilfer its gold and other precious offerings.

One tomb which suffered this fate was
Royal Tomb 779. It was one of the two largest
Woolley discovered and probably originally
one of the richest. Two of its four vaulted
chambers had depressions in the plaster
floor for bodies and there were the disturbed
remains of at least five attendants' bodies,
as well as five guards outside the entrance.
Robbers had broken into the tomb from
above and completely looted its precious
contents. Scraps of gold, silver and lapis
lazuli gave frustrating hints of what had been
lost. But the robbers missed something in
the far corner of the tomb: 'the most elaborate
piece of mosaic and one of the most
remarkable and important objects that the
soil of Mesopotamia has preserved to us'.
Woolley, who wrote these words, thought it
was a standard which had been borne
in processions upon a pole. More likely,
however, it was the sounding box of a harp or
lyre. Complete examples of these instruments
were found in other tombs.

Woolley first came upon the Royal
Cemetery in 1922, but realized that his
workmen were not yet experienced enough
for the delicate work which the 'gold trench'
would involve. So, with incredible restraint,
he delayed excavation for four more years.
That this was time well spent is clear from the
skill Woolley and his men showed in re-
trieving the many crushed and disintegrated
objects they encountered. The shapes of

perished wooden objects were recreated by
pouring liquid plaster into the 'ghost holes'
they left behind in the soil. To recover the
elaborate mosaic inlays which the Sumerians
so loved, Woolley would fix the pieces of
shell and stone together with molten wax
while they were still in the ground. Thus he
was able to lift the panels of the 'standard',
whose original wood and bitumen backings
had long since disintegrated, retaining the
exact juxtapositions of the mosaic pieces.

The main scenes are important documents
of two central themes of Sumerian life and
art: war and banqueting. The war scene
shows the army of Ur led by the king, the
large figure in the centre of the top register.
Behind him stand three bodyguards and his
war chariot, drawn by four equids (probably
asses or ass/onager hybrids). The king
watches as bound prisoners are shepherded
by light-armed troops. In the middle register
we see a file of heavy-armed troops with
metal helmets, short spears and felt (?)
capes; then more light-armed troops, some
wearing only a kilt and bearing a spear or
axe, doing battle with the naked enemy. In
the bottom register are four teams of war
chariots, the three front ones shown riding
roughshod over the bodies of the fallen
enemy. This is one of the earliest illustrations
of the use of the chariot in ancient warfare.

The top register of the banqueting scene
shows the king, again distinguished by his
larger size and flounced skirt, third from the
left. He sits, cup in hand, facing six other
banqueters — perhaps his captains with
whom he is celebrating the victory shown in
the war scene. They are waited on by two
servants (next to the king) and entertained
by a harpist and singer (far right). The
servants would have served beer, which the
Sumerians made from barley and consumed
in copious quantities. The animals and other
goods paraded in the lower registers are
probably booty from the battle or food for the
feast. We are shown (left to right) a small
gazelle, an ibex, a bullock, fish, a herd of
goats, another bullock, sacks of foodstuffs
and equids (probably asses). The men
bearing this booty — probably slaves or
prisoners — are carefully distinguished as

either clean-shaven (the usual Sumerian
practice) or bearded. Some wear what
appear to be feathered head-dresses.

The side panels show vignettes in a more
fanciful vein: real and mythical animals, a
banqueter, and perhaps a herdsman.

Each panel is an elaborate mosaic of
lapis lazuli, red limestone and shell, all set in
bitumen on a wooden frame. Details of the
figures were shown by filling engraved lines
with black pigment (red for the chariots).
Lapis lazuli, together with gold and cornelian,
was one of the Sumerians' favourite luxury
materials, which the rich and powerful would
flaunt, in death as in life, with uninhibited
ostentation. This most valued of stones had
to come all the way from Afghanistan, over
2000 kilometres away. Its abundant use at
this time — lapis lazuli was also popular for
jewellery and cylinder seals — is testimony
to a widespread trading network reaching
as far as the Harappan civilization of the
Indus Valley in modern Pakistan.

Woolley in the Royal Cemetery at Ur, holding the
plaster cast of a disintegrated lyre which he had
just lifted from the soil. (British Museum)

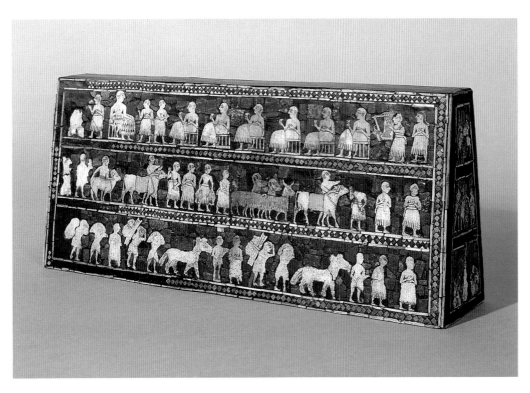

cat. no. **5**

Mesopotamian cylinder seal

Seal with modern impression showing
mythological scene
2334–2193 BC (Akkadian Period)
Mesopotamia (Iraq), findspot unknown
greenstone
3.9 x 2.5 cm diameter
cat. no. 6

The cylinder seal was invented in Mesopotamia around the same time as writing
(see cat. nos 1, 3) and likewise has its
genesis in bureaucratic administration. The
purpose of these stone and shell cylinders,
engraved in negative with elaborate abstract
and figurative designs, was initially not
decorative but functional: to be rolled over
inscribed tablets and the clay sealings
which were packed around jar stoppers,
door handles, bales and other containers,
thus creating a frieze-like impression in the
damp clay. Much like the signet-ring im-
pressions in wax used to seal letters in more
modern times, such sealings acted as a form
of signature, committing the owner to the
transaction or agreement recorded in the
text, and preventing wanton pilfering of
containers and storerooms. These small
cylinders also became the medium for the
first great miniaturist art of antiquity.

This extraordinary seal bears one of the
most elaborate mythological scenes in
Mesopotamian art. Although the precise
meaning of the event portrayed is uncertain
(it may illustrate some myth which has not
survived in writing), the characters can be
identified with reasonable certainty. That
they are all deities is immediately apparent
from their head-dresses of superimposed
sets of bulls' horns; these were worn only by
Mesopotamian gods. A cuneiform inscription
identifies the seal's owner as 'Adda, the
scribe' (ad-da dub-sar).

In the centre of the scene the sun-god
Shamash, rays of light emanating from his
shoulders and holding a saw, is seen rising
from between two mountains, having jour-
neyed by night from the western horizon
through the 'interior of heaven'. Ascending
the mountain on the right is Ea, God of
Wisdom and the Subterranean Waters, distinguished by the streams of flowing water,
replete with fish, which issue from his

shoulders. The bird alighting on his hand is
perhaps Anzu, the monstrous bird who stole
the Tablet of Destinies and was slain by the
warrior-god Ninurta. This fearsome deity
may be the archer at the far left, accompanied
by a roaring lion. Behind Ea stands his
double-faced minister, Usmu. Taking pride
of place upon the mountain in the centre of
the scene is the winged figure of Ishtar, the
goddess of love and war. She is shown full-
face, with battle-axes and maces rising from
her shoulders, and holds what seems to be a
bunch of dates.

Such rich mythological scenes are among
the many innovations of the Akkadian Period,
which witnessed a minor revolution in Mesopotamian art, setting a standard which
artists were to emulate for centuries to come.
A new interest in narrative action — scenes
from daily life as well as royal deeds and
myths — lends the finest works a real
dynamism and vitality. The figures here are
clothed, but scenes showing naked heroes
grappling with beasts display a masterly
control of human and animal anatomy which
was not rivalled until the late Archaic Period
of Greek art. These changes have been seen
as the artistic manifestation of the Semitic
Akkadians' rise to political domination under
Sargon of Agade, and certainly there is a
new emphasis in court art on the king as the
mighty, all-conquering warrior.

By this period, fine seals were clearly
prized as personal ornaments as well as
'signatures' and symbols of office. All but the
very earliest seals had been perforated
length-wise for suspension or attachment to
long copper pins, and in the Akkadian
Period they were often fitted with gold caps
and attachment loops so they could be worn
as pendants or bracelets.

cat. no. 6

Winged genius and sacred tree

Assyrian palace relief
874–860 BC (Neo-Assyrian Period)
from the palace of Ashurnasirpal II, Nimrud,
Assyria (northern Iraq)
gypsum
142 x 94 cm
cat. no. 7

The rediscovery of ancient Assyria in the 1840s and 1850s was the great archaeological sensation of the nineteenth century. Important finds were still being made in Egypt and the Classical lands (including Schliemann's famous discoveries at Troy and Mycenae), but these were now becoming familiar territory. The lands east of the Mediterranean, on the other hand, remained relatively unknown, so that when the English explorer and adventurer Austen Henry Layard set to work on the great city-mounds of northern Mesopotamia he had little idea of what to expect. There were tales of demons buried in the earth, but nothing he had been told prepared Layard for the enormous palaces, with room after room lined with spectacular stone carvings, which were to appear. Within six years he had uncovered a large part of two such palaces, and some rooms of others, at two Assyrian capitals on the River Tigris: Nimrud (ancient Kalhu, biblical Calah) and Nineveh (modern Kuyunjik). In the manner of the day, the most important sculptures were shipped back to London — not without some casualties — where they caused great excitement. Here were the monuments of those very Assyrians who, as the Old Testament relates, had descended with such brutality on the peoples of Israel. For a generation steeped in biblical learning, this held an irresistible fascination.

This relief comes from the six-acre palace which Ashurnasirpal II (see cat. no. 9) built, as he tells us, for his 'lordly pleasure' at Nimrud. It was found in a room where the king would perform ritual ablutions before conducting cultic ceremonies. To celebrate the palace's opening around 864 BC, no less than 69 574 local residents and foreign dignitaries were wined and dined for ten solid days. Not without justification, Ashurnasirpal boasts of his new residence's magnificent interior: 'I decorated it in a splendid fashion ... I made (replicas of) beasts of the mountains and seas in white limestone and alabaster (and) stationed (them) at its doors'.

This slab bears an eagle-headed genius, one of the minor protective deities known to the Assyrians as *apkallu*, meaning 'sages' or 'wise ones'. Other genii had human heads or fish cloaks, but all seem to have served to ward off evil. They are often shown with the king or, as here, flanking a sacred tree — a stylized growth surrounded by a trellis of palmettes, symbolizing some aspect of the earth's fertility. The genii hold a bucket and a 'cone' with which they seem to sprinkle or dust the contents of the bucket onto the sacred tree. The meaning of this curious ritual, repeated countless times on the walls of the Assyrian palaces, is unclear. The 'cone' resembles the male date-palm flower with which the genius here might be fertilizing the sacred tree; but elsewhere they anoint doorways and even the king himself in the same manner. Possibly they are sanctifying these things with holy water.

The genius's clothes — a tasselled robe over a short kilt — resemble those of the king, something no mere mortal was allowed. He wears the usual armlets and bracelets; and the handles of three daggers protrude from the waist of his gown.

The preserved slab is the bottom quarter of a larger block which had two pairs of figures separated by a band of writing recounting the mighty conquests which Ashurnasirpal made when the god Ashur 'placed his merciless weapon in (his) lordly arms'. Another eagle-headed genius sprinkled the other side of the sacred tree. Then, above the inscription, a pair of kneeling, human-headed genii touched the palmettes of another sacred tree. This symmetrical scheme was repeated around most of the room, interrupted only by two female figures who stood guard near a drain.

The reliefs were originally painted, at least in parts, but the colour rarely survives. Layard reported red on the tongue of another eagle-headed genius.

Like the Egyptians, Assyrian relief sculptors conceived their figures essentially in two dimensions. Everything is shown either frontally or in profile, and unavoidable transitions — like the shoulder here — are not handled well. Anatomy is quite keenly observed, but not with the aim of achieving a life-like representation. Muscles, veins and sinews, especially on the genius's legs, are deliberately simplified and exaggerated to enhance their decorative qualities. So too the painstaking detailing of feathers, hair and tasselled hems are more exercises in interesting patterning than in realistic effects. Yet despite this emphasis on decoration, the figures retain the massive, ungainly air which typifies so much Assyrian art. It was left for the Achaemenid Persians to refine them into more elegant images.

cat. no. 7

King Ashurnasirpal II hunting lions

Assyrian palace relief
874–860 BC (Neo-Assyrian Period)
from the palace of Ashurnasirpal II, Nimrud,
Assyria (northern Iraq)
gypsum
1.0 x 1.4 m

cat. no. 8

Mesopotamian kings throughout history prided themselves on their prowess as hunters, and no victim proved their strength and bravery better than the lion. The king of beasts was both the natural symbol of sovereignty — kings are often likened to lions in descriptions of warfare — and the most challenging prey for a ruler of men. A number of Assyrian kings are shown in their palace reliefs hunting these noble beasts, which are graphically rendered in the throes of death with great feeling and respect, if not quite sympathy. Pierced by arrows and gushing blood, they collapse on the ground, overtaken by the superior strength and valour of the 'king of the world'.

In this relief we see Ashurnasirpal II speeding along in his chariot, his bow drawn at some hapless victim — no doubt another lion — which was represented in the next slab. The three horses of the chariot team are shown galloping in unison over a cowering lion, snarling in agony at the three arrows which have struck home. Chariots would have overturned on such large obstacles, and this common artistic device (see cat. nos 5 and 15) is not to be taken literally.

The relief was found by the Assyriologist Henry Layard in the west wing of the state apartments of Ashurnasirpal's palace at Nimrud. He came upon it, resting face-down on the floor, while digging a trench to remove one of the enormous winged bulls which guarded the main doorways — perhaps the very one shown in the illustration on page 14 . Struck by the relief's brilliant 'finish, the elegance of its ornaments, and the great spirit of the design', Layard regarded it as one of 'the most perfect hitherto discovered in Assyria', and this is no less true today. The king in his chariot is a standard formula, but the dying lion — its face contorted in an agonized roar, cowering with its tail between its legs as one paw claws vainly forward — is a dramatic and evocative image of a proud beast's noble death. The stance and movement are keenly observed from nature, rising above the artistic clichés of some cultic and mythological scenes (cat. no. 7). Assyrian art, so often preoccupied with the formal dignity and grandeur of the king and court, evokes in animal studies like this an emotionally charged atmosphere of drama rarely rivalled in ancient art.

This emphasis on the king and his exploits — doing battle or hunting, performing cultic ceremonies, or just reclining in his garden — was a new departure in official Mesopotamian art, which had before focused mainly on the gods and their worship. The reason lies in the essentially propagandistic purpose of the reliefs: to impress upon foreign dignitaries and other visitors the incomparable power and authority of the king. And it must surely have worked. We can well imagine how ambassadors from distant provinces of the empire, led along corridors lined at every turn with visible proof of the king's invincible power, would have been awed — if they were not already — into a sense of helpless submission.

As with humans and humanoid demons (cat. no. 7), the animals' limbs and joints become to the Assyrian sculptor an exercise in decorative dissection. In this relief, the sculptor has concentrated particularly on the complex pattern of tendons in the lion's rear legs. Unlike the Egyptian convention, where both halves of dual elements had always to be shown (see cat. no. 22), Assyrian profile views are often simplified by ignoring the farther of paired limbs (the horses each have only two legs) and wheels.

At the top of the scene are the last two lines of an inscription detailing Ashurnasirpal's achievements. Above this, the upper part of the slab originally bore another illustrated frieze.

cat. no. 8

37

Ashurnasirpal II, King of Assyria

Assyrian statue
874–860 BC (Neo-Assyrian Period)
from the temple of Ishtar, Nimrud, Assyria
(northern Iraq)
limestone
1.06 m height (figure only)
cat. no. 9

'Ashurnasirpal, great king, mighty king, king of the universe' — thus the inscription on this statue identifies itself to the world. And for once this royal conceit has some basis. When Ashurnasirpal (the name means 'the god Ashur is guardian of the heir') ascended the throne in 883 BC, Assyria had been in decline for two centuries, her dominions reduced to little more than the ancient heartland — a mere eighty by one-hundred-and-sixty-kilometre strip along the Tigris River. When he died twenty-five years later, Assyria was indisputably the greatest power in the ancient world, its mere name enough to inspire dread and fear from the shores of the eastern Mediterranean to Persia. Ashurnasirpal inaugurated the last and most glorious period in Assyria's history, when all the Near East became the hunting-ground of Ashur's protégés, descending on the Israelites and other peoples, as Byron so vividly put it, 'like the wolf on the fold'.

Although the Assyrians lined the walls of their palaces lavishly with sculptured stone friezes (cat. nos 7, 8), they did not so favour free-standing statuary, except for the essential cult images in temples (and these, being usually of gold and other precious materials, do not survive). Only a handful of sizeable royal statues are known, of which this — the only one of Ashurnasirpal — is certainly the finest.

The statue embodies well the calculated frightfulness which Ashurnasirpal developed to such a fine art in warfare. As one historian has said:

> There is no smile, no piety, almost no humanity in the statue but the rigid attitude of a conceited despot, the aquiline nose of a bird of prey, the straight-looking eyes of a chief who demands absolute obedience.

He is shown without the usual cylindrical felt crown, allowing us to see the regimented ringlets of his long, neat hair. His clothing is the form of dress worn by the king on ceremonial occasions: a long rectangular shawl wrapped around the body and tied at the waist with a cord sewn to one corner. In his hands he holds symbols of sovereignty: a mace (still at this time a weapon of war) and curved crook-axe.

The statue was found by the pioneer Assyriologist Henry Layard during his excavations at Nimrud (ancient Kalhu, biblical Calah) in Assyria. Early in his reign Ashurnasirpal chose Nimrud as the site for his new capital, building there a magnificent palace and a number of temples. These included a shrine to Ishtar, the goddess of love and war. Mesopotamian deities often had various names and attributes at different places, and the Ishtar worshipped at Nimrud was known as Sharrat-nipkhi, meaning 'queen of the rising (star)'. It was here in Ishtar's shrine in 1850 that Layard came across Ashurnasirpal's statue, lying in a large recess paved with a monumental inscribed alabaster slab (3.6 x 6.0 metres), exactly as it had fallen nearly 3000 years earlier.

Layard, like all educated men of the day, saw the monuments of Assyria through eyes attuned to Classical art, a standard by which they inevitably paled. 'The features', he said of this piece, 'were majestic, and the general proportions of the statue not altogether incorrect'. But, he went on, there is 'a want of breadth in the side view peculiar to Assyrian works of art of this nature'. His point is right: Assyrian sculptures, even statues in the round, were conceived essentially in two planes, to be viewed only from the front in their original settings. But that is not something the Assyrians — for whom monumental art was first and foremost an exercise in propaganda — would have thought a defect.

And we may now agree. Square on, despite the less than life-size scale, Ashurnasirpal strikes an effectively fearsome image. Looking at him, we can well believe his rage at those unfortunates who, as he tells us, 'did not seize (his) feet' — the usual token of submission. His annals speak of rebel leaders being ruthlessly flayed alive and their skins hung on the walls of Nineveh. One town in south-eastern Anatolia lost 3000 men in battle, but they, as it turned out, were the lucky ones: of the prisoners taken alive, some were burnt to death and others were mutilated.

> I cut off their arms and hands, others their noses, ears and extremities. I gouged out the eyes of many troops. I made one pile of the living and one pile of the dead. I hung their heads on trees around the city. I burnt their adolescent boys and girls.

Ashurnasirpal was not the first or last great monarch of the ancient world to indulge in such orgies of cruelty, but he was exceptional in the sadistic pleasure he seemed to take in the retelling.

Entrance to the temple of Ishtar at the time of its discovery. (British Museum)

Assyrian cylinder seals

Seal with modern impression showing winged
genius between winged bulls
c.730 BC (Neo-Assyrian Period)
Mesopotamia (Iraq), findspot unknown
cornelian
3.7 x 1.7 cm diameter

cat. no. 10

Seal with modern impression showing the
goddess Ishtar with worshipper and ibexes
c.730 BC (Neo-Assyrian Period)
Mesopotamia (Iraq), findspot unknown
green garnet
4.3 x 1.8 cm diameter

cat. no. 11

The cylinder-seal engravers of the Neo-Assyrian Period (ninth to seventh centuries BC) pursued their art — by then some 2500 years old — to new heights of technical sophistication, producing some of the most finely detailed and decorative cylinders of all time. As the stamp seal was now becoming increasingly popular, their work represents the last period of large-scale cylinder-seal production.

In the finest works of the period, like these two pieces, great care was taken by engravers to capture the details of dress and anatomy which their sculptor colleagues rendered with such meticulous care in the full-scale palace wall reliefs (cat. nos 7, 8). In the manner of Assyrian art, much of this detail is highly stylized: the winged genius's hair and the bulls' belly fur are reduced to regimented rows of curls; and the crossed ibexes' beards and the date-palm fronds become sets of simple chevrons. As on the palace reliefs, the animals are in general treated with a more straightforward naturalism than the human figures, who must affect a formal dignity and authority. The faithfully delineated tendons, flexed muscles and keenly observed heads give the beasts on these cylinders a life-like quality and animation which belies their diminutive proportions. Fine detail like this could only be engraved on hard stones which would take a clear, sharp edge. The seal cutters of this period favoured chalcedonies and other translucent coloured stones, which they engraved with a bronze cutting wheel and drills, feeding in emery as an abrasive.

The genius between the winged bulls on the first seal (cat. no. 10) brings together two enduring strains in Mesopotamian art: decorative symmetry and man's mastery over nature. The winged genius, a favourite character in palace relief sculpture, was one of the protective deities who guarded the king and his palace from danger. The winged bulls he masters here must be evil forces of some kind, though elsewhere they can be benevolent.

Seal inscriptions were usually cut as mirror images so that when they were impressed in clay the impression would read normally. In this period, however, as seals were worn increasingly as decorations or amulets, the inscriptions tended to be cut into the cylinder in normal lettering so that the impression produced a mirror image. That is how this text has been treated. It reads: 'Let him who trusts you not be put to shame, O Nabu! Let him follow you. Make (him) enjoy wealth, increase (his) life'.

The second seal (cat. no. 11) shows Ishtar, the goddess of love and war, standing on her sacred lion, receiving a worshipper. The goddess is shown in military dress, much as King Ashurbanipal (668–631 BC) described her appearing to one of his seers in a dream: 'on (her) right and left she had quivers, she held a bow in her hand, a sharp sword she held unsheathed for battle'. Here, however, the goddess's sword is tucked into her belt in a star-tipped sheath. Behind it hangs a crescent-shaped sickle-sword with seven dots (a magical number in Mesopotamia).

The star atop Ishtar's crown, echoed by others on the tips of her crossed quivers and sheath, is the symbol of Venus, the planet she represents. The feature hovering in the sky above the worshipper, looking like another astral body, is in fact a type of ear-ring. Its meaning here is not clear. The pair of crossed ibexes, a very old Mesopotamian motif which had first appeared on cylinder seals some 2000 years earlier, is added simply for decorative value and does not relate to the main cult scene.

Assyrian seals with worshippers being received by deities were often owned by highly placed court officials. Although this one is not inscribed, its fine workmanship suggests an owner of considerable status.

cat. no. 10   cat. no. 11

The Flood Tablet

Assyrian tablet inscribed with part of the
Babylonian story paralleling the biblical account
of Noah's Ark
c.650 BC (Neo-Assyrian Period)
from the palace of Ashurbanipal, Nineveh,
Assyria (northern Iraq)
clay
13.7 x 13.0 cm
cat. no. 12

Of all the thousands of tablets discovered in the libraries of the Assyrian kings at Nineveh, none caused such a sensation as the Flood Tablet. The story of its rediscovery by an intrepid young assistant in the British Museum is an extraordinary tale of luck and adventure.

George Smith's Assyriological career began when an official at the British Museum noticed his intense interest in the sculptures from the excavations of the Assyrian capitals. He was given a junior position and set to finding joins among the 20 000 fragmentary cuneiform texts from Ashurbanipal's library (mostly copies of older Babylonian and Sumerian works) discovered at Nineveh in the 1840s and 1850s. One day in 1872, as Smith later described, he came across

> a curious tablet which had evidently contained originally six columns ... On looking down the third column, my eye caught the statement that the ship rested on the mountains of Nizir, followed by the account of the sending forth of the dove, and its finding no resting-place and returning. I saw at once that I had here discovered a portion at least of the Chaldean [Babylonian] account of the Deluge.

A Babylonian Noah! Smith, a rather nervous and excitable character, could not contain himself. 'I am the first man to read that after more than two thousand years of oblivion!', he exclaimed. Then, 'setting the tablet on the table, he jumped up and rushed out of the room in a great state of excitement and, to the astonishment of those present, began to undress himself!'.

Public reaction to Smith's sensational discovery was hardly less dramatic. The scholarly community and the public alike were captivated by the thought of biblical history coming graphically to life through the records of the ancient Assyrians. The

London *Daily Telegraph* offered 1000 guineas to fund an expedition to find the missing portion of the story. Smith eagerly accepted and headed off to Nineveh in January 1873. With incredible luck, after only a week's work, he found a fragment from another tablet bearing most of the missing section of the story among the debris from the previous diggings (such was the carelessness of the early excavators!). But the story has a tragic end. Returning from Nineveh through Syria after an abortive expedition three years later, Smith succumbed to dysentery and died in Aleppo at the early age of thirty-six.

The Noah of the Babylonian flood story turned out to be called Utnapishtim (meaning 'I have found eternal life'), who tells his tale to the legendary hero Gilgamesh. Distraught at the death of his great friend Enkidu and obsessed with the thought of his own mortality, Gilgamesh seeks out Utnapishtim to learn how he has been able to avoid the fate of all other mortals. Utnapishtim duly explains how Enlil, the lord of the gods, had been disturbed by mankind and sent a devastating flood to decimate the world. But Ea, the god of wisdom, took pity on the pious Utnapishtim who, like his biblical counterpart, was instructed how to build a great boat into which he brought 'all the living beings' — 'the beasts of the field' and 'the wild creatures of the field' — as well as all his family and craftsmen. At the end of the story, after 'all of mankind had returned to clay' and the waters had receded, the dutiful Utnapishtim offered sacrifices to the gods. Pacified by his piety, Enlil took Utnapishtim and his wife aboard the ship and made them kneel, touching their foreheads as he blessed them: 'Hitherto Utnapishtim has been but human. Henceforth Utnapishtim and his wife shall be like unto us gods'. Thus was the godly man admitted to the realm of the immortals.

A half-century after Smith's discovery, it was found that an early section of the Sumerian King List, preserved on clay tablets, interrupts the monotonous recitation of dynasties and rulers with the statement: '(Then) the Flood swept over (the earth)'. Here, it seemed, was historical proof of this

catastrophic event, and some archaeologists were tempted to look for evidence of a great deluge in excavations at Sumerian sites. And indeed they soon found it: thick layers of water-borne silt sandwiched between the remains of successive settlements. One such deposit was found at Shuruppak, Utnapishtim's home town, dating to about 2800 BC. But silt layers occurred at other sites at different dates; the thickest of all (over three metres) devastated Ur over 1000 years earlier. Indeed, flooding was a recurrent danger in Sumer and there seem to have been a number of catastrophic inundations affecting various settlements from time to time. But there is so far no evidence of a flood which affected all of Sumer, nor any definite link between any of the flood levels that have been found and the deluge of Babylonian literature. From an archaeological point of view, *the* flood remains unproven, and many now explain the story as a literary creation, though one which drew on widespread experience of this common phenomenon.

Since Smith's day, earlier Mesopotamian versions of the flood story, in both Babylonian and Sumerian, have come to light. The earliest of these texts date to the seventeenth century BC, but the story itself may be much older. A few tablets which were inscribed almost a thousand years earlier and bear editions of other Sumerian literary compositions have already been found.

cat. no. **12**

Royal inscription of King Nebuchadnezzar II

Babylonian inscribed tablet
604–562 BC (Neo-Babylonian Period)
Babylon, Mesopotamia (Iraq)
limestone
58.0 x 50.5 x 10.0 cm
cat. no. 13

Nebuchadnezzar — or Nabu-kudurri-usur as his name was written in Babylonian — is one of the few Mesopotamian rulers whose place in history did not have to await the birth of modern archaeology. Razing Jerusalem to the ground and driving its inhabitants into exile in Babylon, this mightiest of the Babylonian kings to rule Mesopotamia after the fall of Assyria was the architect of events which left an indelible mark on the Jews' historical consciousness. While in Babylon the Hebrew scribes committed much of the Old Testament to writing, including an account of their recent deportation. And so the fame — or infamy — of this most magnificent of the Babylonian kings was assured.

For the Babylonians, the Jews were just another troublesome people and their deportation a standard stratagem which rarely merited attention in royal annals. This inscription is a commemorative text celebrating deeds much closer to Nebuchadnezzar's heart: his piety to the gods and the grand building programs he undertook in Babylonia. His most lavish projects were in Babylon itself — at 850 hectares, the largest city ever in Mesopotamia's long history. The king restored many of Babylon's temples, including the shrine of the chief Babylonian deity Marduk, which, as he says near the end of the second column of this inscription, he 'caused to shine like the sun', covering the interior walls with 'bright gold, lapis lazuli and alabaster'.

But Nebuchadnezzar was most proud of the magnificent new palace which he built beside, and connecting with, the old royal apartments. Near the end of this inscription (the eighth and ninth columns) he describes in detail how he raised up a 'great dwelling for my royal residence' atop a series of walls and embankments:

> In a favourable month, on a propitious day, I laid out its foundation on the edge of the Underworld; I made its top as high as a mountain ... For its roof I laid out great cedar beams, the produce of high mountains, strong firs and fine choice cypresses. At all its gates I set up doors of *musukkannu*-wood, cedar, cypress, ebony (?) and ivory, set with silver and gold, (and) bound in bronze ... I had a battlement of blue enamelled bricks built around its top. I built around it ... a great wall of mighty stones, hewn from great mountains, and I raised its head like a mountain. I made the residence a source of wonder for all people to behold; I filled it with splendour. Dignity, anger, the terrifying splendour of kingship encircle it. The wicked and unrighteous may not enter!

Surprisingly, however, there is no mention in this or any other contemporary documents of the construction for which Nebuchadnezzar was most famous in Classical times and later — the renowned Hanging Gardens. Counted among the Seven Wonders of the ancient world, these gardens are described by Hellenistic and Roman authors as a series of wooded terraces which the king supposedly built to remind his Median (Persian) wife of her mountain homeland. A series of sturdy vaulted chambers uncovered in the corner of the Old (Southern) Palace was believed by their German excavator to be part of the garden's substructure, but this has been thrown into doubt, and no other remains which can definitely be linked to the gardens have since been found.

Nebuchadnezzar's tablet ends with a prayer to his patron deity, for whom he had done so much to glorify Babylon.

> O Marduk, wise lord of the gods, almighty prince, you created me and entrusted to me kingship over all people. I love your exalted form as my own precious life. I have not exalted any city among all habitations more than your city Babylon. As I love your terrifying divinity and seek out your lordship, receive my prayer graciously, hear my supplication. I am the king, the benefactor who gladdens your heart, the wise governor, the benefactor of all your shrines. At your command, O merciful Marduk, may the house which I have built flourish forever; may I be satisfied with its luxury; may I reach old age within it; may I enjoy extreme old age; may I receive within it the weighty tribute of the kings of the world, of all peoples. From the horizon to the zenith, wherever [the sun-god] Shamash goes, may I have no enemies; may I encounter no rebels; may my descendants rule the black-headed (people) within it [the palace] forever!

But of course even this greatest of the Babylonians had to contend with rebellion, as the Bible graphically relates. Having wrested control of Mesopotamia from the Assyrians, Nebuchadnezzar was forced to fight long and hard to maintain Assyria's network of provinces in Syria and Palestine (Judah), leading a number of campaigns as far as the borders of Egypt. More than once the Egyptians, Babylon's great rivals, were defeated and forced to retreat, and it was they who inspired two kings of Judah to revolt in the space of only ten years. The response was swift and brutal. First Jehoiakin — finding himself thrust to the head of a revolt by his father's untimely death just as the Babylonians were approaching — was carted off to Babylon (597 BC), along with most of his family and the leading citizens; then his uncle Zedekiah, who had been placed on the throne by Nebuchadnezzar, repeated his predecessor's folly, bringing total destruction upon Jerusalem (586 BC) and a painful exile upon its people. Zedekiah tried to escape but the Babylonians caught him up, and the punishment for compounding his brother's foolhardiness with treachery was to be severe. Bringing him before the king of Babylon, 'they slew the sons of Zedekiah before his eyes, and put out his eyes, and bound him in fetters of brass, and carried him off to Babylon'.

Cuneiform writing on clay, the cheap everyday medium, was often so cramped that only the trained specialist can see where one sign ends and another begins (see cat. no. 12). Important royal inscriptions like this tablet, intended for public display or burial in the foundations of buildings (where the gods and future kings would see them), were often carved in stone and more carefully articulated, the scribes clearly taking pride in the clarity and beauty of their engraving. This text was probably originally buried in the foundations of one of Nebuchadnezzar's numerous constructions.

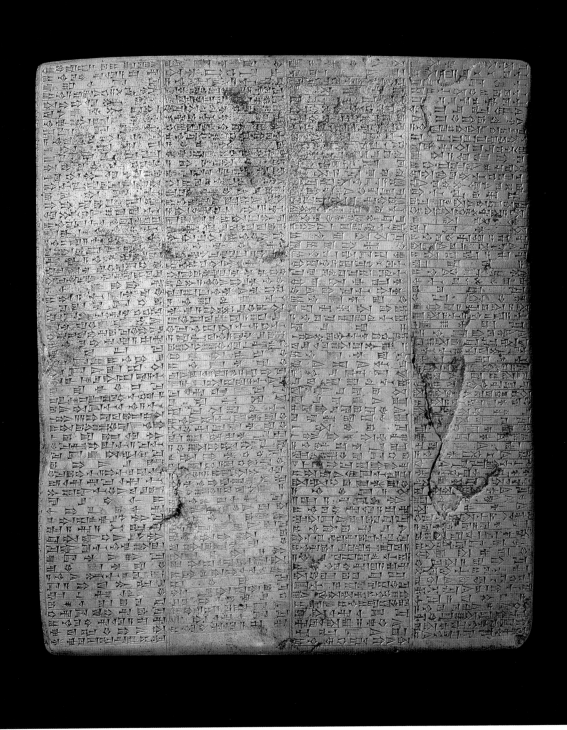

cat. no. 13

Persian griffin bracelet

c.550–400 BC (Achaemenid Period) from the Oxus Treasure, Bactria (Soviet Central Asia) gold, originally inlaid with lazulite (?) and other stones
12.7 cm diameter

cat. no. 14

This striking bracelet is one of an identical pair which came to light in 1877 as part of the Oxus Treasure, named after the river (now known as the Amu Darya) near which it was found. Much of the treasure, like the bracelets, may be dated on the basis of style to the Achaemenid Period, but other pieces said to have been found with it (some, especially the coins, may be strays from other finds) suggest that the hoard was not finally buried for some centuries, perhaps around 180 BC.

The Oxus armlets have been justly placed among 'the great masterpieces of the jeweller's art'. Almost solid at the bottom where the ring is indented, they become hollow towards the terminals. These are decorated with horned and winged griffins (compare cat. no. 16) whose elaborately patterned bodies were originally inlaid with coloured stones. Of this sophisticated *cloisonné* and *champlevé* work, only a single piece of blue stone survives on one of the wings. The brilliant effect of the golden beasts when fully coloured must have been truly dazzling.

The Achaemenids' genius for adapting natural forms to dramatic decorative effect is seen here at its very best. The griffins emerge gradually from the ring, the low relief of the hind legs and tails giving way to a fully sculptural treatment of the forequarters. Following the smooth curve of the armlet, they spring towards each other in imminent collision, though the heraldic symmetry serves to negate any real sense of movement. Anatomical detail — whether of clawed feet, musculature or feathers — is everywhere made an excuse for elegant patterning. The solid forms rendered in gold are modelled with that controlled gracefulness and sharp definition of contour which gives the best Achaemenid work such an air of slick professionalism. This is clearly the work of a master-craftsman and must have belonged to a high-ranking official or member of the royal family.

As in the griffin drinking vessel (cat. no. 16), traces may be seen of the diverse sources from which Achaemenid craftsmen drew their inspiration. Griffins have a long Mesopotamian ancestry but the barbaric ferocity and exuberance of these beasts, as well as details like the thickening of the ends of the horns and the polychrome inlays, reflect the impact of the arts of the nomadic Scythians who roamed the steppes of Central Asia (see cat. no. 18).

The recovery of the Oxus Treasure and its near escape from the melting pot is an extraordinary tale which centres around one Captain F.C. Burton, a British officer who proved himself to be a quite exceptional character. The adventure begins in 1880, when its finders sold the hoard to three Muslim merchants from Bukhara. On the way to Afghanistan, where they intended to sell the treasure, the merchants were attacked and robbed by bandits. The robbers made for the hills, taking the merchants and their servant with them, but after they arrived at a cave to divide the spoil, the servant was able to escape. Burton, as it happened, was stationed nearby, and when told by the servant of the day's events immediately set off after the culprits with two orderlies. He arrived at the cave around midnight to find four of the bandits wounded from squabbling over the division of the spoil, which was already being cut up and prepared for melting. With the incredible bravado that only a Victorian Englishman could have mustered, Burton managed by threats to persuade the robbers to surrender a large part of the treasure. He then made a hasty exit, but having been warned that the robbers might try to ambush him and regain their booty, Burton hid by night and only returned home at dawn. He then threatened to raise a force against the bandits, but they, hearing this, averted another confrontation with the formidable Englishman by offering up a further large part of the treasure. This brought the total recovered to about three-quarters.

All this treasure Burton magnanimously returned to the merchants, asking only that he be permitted to buy the griffin bracelet which he saw in one of the open bags. Burton later gave the bracelet — the matching pair to the piece displayed here — to the Victoria and Albert Museum in London. The rest of the hoard — over 180 items — the merchants sold in the bazaar at Rawalpindi in present-day Pakistan. Fortunately, much of it was eventually bought by General Alexander Cunningham, a British soldier and archaeologist, who later sold it to Sir Wollaston Franks, a keeper at the British Museum. Franks died in 1897, bequeathing the treasure to the Museum.

Recent excavations suggest that the treasure probably came from the palace-temple at Takht-i Sangin in Bactria (Soviet Central Asia).

cat. no. 14

Persian cylinder seal

Seal with modern impression showing
King Darius hunting lions
c.522–400 BC (Achaemenid Period)
Egypt (Thebes?)
agate
3.7 x 1.6 cm diameter

cat. no. 15

This seal, showing a Persian king hunting lions, is one of the few cylinder seals inscribed with a royal name to have survived from the ancient Near East. The inscription records the king's name and title — 'Darius, the Great King' — in three languages: Old Persian, Elamite and Babylonian (Akkadian). There were three kings of the Achaemenid Dynasty called Darius. This one is probably the first, Darius the Great (521–486 BC); less likely is Darius II (423–405 BC).

Even without the inscription, the masterly engraving and choice of subject would mark this seal as the product of a royal workshop. Hunting was a favourite pastime of Near Eastern kings, and scenes of the chase, emphasizing the king's valour, are a recurrent cliché in the arts of the region. Here we see Darius in his chariot, bow drawn, speeding towards a rampant lion. The horses are shown galloping over the body of another slain lion, a conventional if unrealistic way of representing triumph over a defeated foe, adopted from Mesopotamia (see cat. nos 5 and 8). The winged figure hovering above recalls the similar representations of a Mesopotamian god who accompanies Assyrian rulers into battle. Here, however, it probably represents a deity of Persian origin: Ahura-mazda, the chief god of the Achaemenids and the godhead of later Zoroastrianism. Although it is unclear whether the Achaemenid kings were themselves thorough-going Zoroastrians, it was under their rule that the faith took firm hold in Iran.

Zoroaster (or Zarathustra as he was called in Persian), the prophet of the new religion, proclaimed Ahura-mazda (Wise Lord) as sole deity and creator of all things. He embodied goodness and light against the forces of evil and darkness, a conflict of opposites that lay at the heart of the Zoroastrian world view. Zoroastrian worship centred around fire-temples, the eternal flame symbolizing purity and truth. To the horror of the Greeks, they exposed their dead on platforms to be devoured by carrion before burial, since the sacred flame would be corrupted by cremation. Descendants of the Zoroastrians still keep these practices alive in parts of Iran and in western India, where they are known today as Parsees.

By the time of the Achaemenid Empire, the traditional cylinder seal was being superseded by stamp seals and engraved metal finger-rings. Such, it seems, was the seal carried and used by the Achaemenid king as his personal mark — probably a gold finger-ring with an engraved face. But cylinder seals inscribed with the king's name continued to be issued to high court officials for 'signing' documents and administering affairs with royal authority. Others again were apparently presented by the king to loyal officials for outstanding service. The owner of this cylinder must have been one such senior official or royal favourite.

Persian drinking horn

c.500–330 BC (Achaemenid Period)
Armenia, reportedly near Erzincan (north-eastern Turkey)
silver, partly gilded
25.2 cm height
cat. no. 16

The peoples of metal-rich Persia were among the most advanced and talented metalsmiths of antiquity. A long tradition of fine crafts-manship in copper, silver and gold reached its climax under the Achaemenid Dynasty (559–331 BC) in pieces, such as this horn-shaped drinking vessel (rhyton), that rank among the most striking and elegant plate ever made. The splendour of Achaemenid metalwork was proverbial among the Greeks who recounted with awe the 'many golden bowls, goblets and other drinking vessels' captured from the Persian camp at the Battle of Plataea, 479 BC. Even this was but a foretaste of the phenomenal treasures that awaited Alexander the Great when he looted the great Persian capitals a century and a half later.

Rhyton drinking vessels occur in the Near East long before the Achaemenid Period, but the Persian metalsmiths made the form particularly their own, the success of their creations inspiring the Greeks and other peoples to adopt it also. Under the Achaemenid Empire, Persian arts and practices were widely disseminated to provinces like Turkey, where this rhyton was found. By the standards of the day, Achaemenid rule was firm but tolerant, and local officials in these regions often adopted Persian customs and ornaments.

Earlier Mesopotamian rhyta, often ending in an animal's head, tended to be straight; the Achaemenid bent form harks back to the bulls' horns from which they were origin-ally carved. Like many such rhyta, this vessel was used as a drinking funnel. Wine poured in the top came out in a narrow stream through a small hole between the griffin's legs. This could be fed into a drinking cup or, holding the rhyton up, straight into the drinker's mouth.

The griffin takes the typically Achaemenid form, with horns, a vulture's beak and a crest down the back of the neck. The cavities in the eyes, in the chest pendant, and along the crest were originally set with coloured inlays (probably gems), heightening further the dramatically sumptuous effect of the decoration.

As is typical of Achaemenid art, this decoration is at once derivative and highly original. The Achaemenids drew heavily on the arts of their neighbours and prede-cessors: the Assyrians and Babylonians, whom they succeeded as the dominant power of the ancient world; the nomadic Scythians of the northern steppe-lands; and, to a lesser extent, the Urartians of Armenia and the Greeks. From Mesopo-tamia came much of their iconography and many modes of representation. The elegant stylization of animal and floral forms which is the keynote of Achaemenid art follows directly in the Neo-Babylonian, Assyrian and ultimately Akkadian traditions. But the Achaemenids tuned the Mesopotamian formulas to a new pitch of stately elegance. Under the influence of the Animal Style (see cat. no. 18), they achieved a more severe reduction of natural forms and textures to graceful curves and patterns. The line is more confident, the detail sharper and the proportions more carefully balanced than ever before. In works like this rhyton, the stylizing tendency which had dominated Mesopotamian art for almost two millennia can be seen pursued to its logical con-clusion — the aesthetics of idealized gracefulness.

Historically, too, Achaemenid art repre-sented the end of a tradition. When Alexander the Great defeated the last Achaemenid king, Darius III, he opened the Near East to a very different philosophy of art which valued naturalism and expression above all else, and conceived of everything in human form. With the spread of Hellenism, first under Alexander's successors and later under the Romans, a three-thousand-year-old tradition gradually faded from view. The indigenous styles that next emerged in Persia under the Parthians, the Sasanians and finally under Islam drew their inspiration from other sources and were only incidentally affected by the ancient Near Eastern legacy.

The rhyton is made of silver which was cast and beaten in two pieces, the fluted bowl fitting into the rear of the griffin's body, before being partly fire gilded.

cat. no. 16

Worshipper

Persian or Greco-Bactrian statuette
c.500–300 BC (Achaemenid or early Hellenistic Period)
from the Oxus Treasure, Bactria (Soviet Central Asia)
silver, partly gilded
29.2 cm height

cat. no. 17

When Alexander the Great, King of Macedon, conquered the Persian Empire in the late fourth century BC, he opened the East to the arts and culture of Greece. Thoroughly steeped in Greek culture himself (his tutor was none other than Aristotle), Alexander settled groups of veteran troops at strategic points throughout the newly won territories, founding or refounding cities in the name of Hellenism. This process was continued by the heir to his eastern domains, his general Seleucus. The easternmost lands — Mesopotamia, Persia and Bactria — were the first to break away from Macedonian control in the fighting which followed Alexander's premature death. But even in the short space of fifty years, while they formed part of the great Seleucid kingdom, Greek culture took firm root. Ironically, it was in Bactria and western India — the most remote parts of Alexander's empire — that, through the tenacious independence of the settlers, the impact of Greek art was strongest and most enduring.

The mixing of Greek and Oriental traditions had some unlikely results: coins with Greek designs but inscriptions in the Central Asian Kharoshti script; Buddhas with the perfect faces and flowing drapery of a Greek god. Is this unusual statuette from the Oxus Treasure (which included also cat. nos 14 and 18) another, perhaps earlier, artistic meeting of East and West? Its heroic nudity, votive stance and tentative naturalism were commonplace in Greek art (cat. no. 65) but are little known at this time in Iran or Mesopotamia, where ritual nudity is rarely depicted after Sumerian times (third millennium BC). Some scholars have therefore seen in this work influence from the Greek world on a Persian artist of the Achaemenid Period or the free mixing of traditions by a Greco-Bactrian craftsman some time after Alexander. The idea of showing the figure naked may indeed have come from Greece, but there the close resemblance stops. The sculptor does not, like contemporary Greeks, approach the nude as a naturalistic challenge. Representing the figure naked, he is obliged to give some plausible form to the muscles; but he shows no interest in going further. The face too — wide-eyed and characterless — is a standardized formula in the Near Eastern tradition, devoid of any hint of individuality. The figure is a symbol, nothing more, though this does not detract from its naive charm. All in all, despite the formal links, the spirit of the piece is much more Oriental than Greek and fits happily into an Achaemenid cultural context.

The only article of attire is a strange hat rendered in gold. A similar headgear is represented on other items from the Oxus Treasure — these are also of Achaemenid date — but it is not clear what status or role it indicates. This figure's stance — presenting with both hands some lost offering — would perhaps be most appropriate to the image of a mortal making a dedication.

The body and head were made separately and soldered together. Both were cast solid. The pierced ears may have held earrings, probably gold like the hat.

cat. no. **17**

'Scythian' hood or turban ornament

c.400–200 BC (Achaemenid or
Hellenistic Period)
from the Oxus Treasure, Bactria (Soviet
Central Asia)
gold
6.2 cm length
cat. no. 18

The vast Eurasian steppe-lands stretching some 7000 kilometres from eastern Europe to the borders of China were occupied in antiquity by hordes of nomads referred to today as Scythians. Having left no written records of their own, these peoples enter history only when they impinge on the lives of their settled neighbours to the south, usually as marauding invaders. But where history fails us, archaeology has provided ample compensation; the burial mounds which litter the plains of Central Asia reveal a great deal about the material culture of these fierce horse-riding pastoralists. They are renowned above all for their sophisticated and original metalwork, dominated by what has come to be known as the Animal Style. As long ago as the fifth century BC the Greek historian Herodotus remarked upon the glittering gold ornaments which one Central Asian tribe, the Massagetae, lavished upon their headgear, belts and chestbands. And like horsemen everywhere their animals were not forgotten: 'They give their horses bronze breastplates, and use gold about the bridle, bit and cheek-pieces'.

The Animal-Style ornament shown here comes from the Oxus Treasure, a Central Asian temple-hoard of mainly Achaemenid goldwork (see also cat. nos 14, 17). It is an openwork convex plaque, elaborately embossed and chased, which was probably worn as a hood or turban ornament, attached by means of two long pins which project from the back.

The animal represented is a mythical hybrid with a deer's body, eagle's wings, long curved horns and a horse's ears. This odd zoological hotchpotch was probably inspired by the lion-griffin, a Persian invention of Achaemenid times, and shows that the artist was acquainted with Persian art. But the liberties he takes in adapting the standard griffin — replacing the usual lion's body, eagle's claws and scorpion's tail with a deer's body and hoofs, and a tail ending in a leaf — confirm what is apparent from the style: this is not the work of an Achaemenid artist. Its spirit belongs rather to the art of the nomads of the northern steppe-lands. Such free mixing of Persian and Scythian traditions was probably the work of an artist somewhere on the far limits of Achaemenid control in Central Asia (modern Afghanistan or southern Soviet Central Asia), where ancient Classical authors place the Sacae, Massagetae and other nomadic Scythian tribes.

The monster's legs bend back on themselves like rubber, displaying a disregard for anatomy which is typical of the Animal Style's unrestrained approach. Even in their more realistic works, steppe artists would not hesitate to bend and twist animals' bodies into impossibly contorted poses. If a circular design was desired, the whole body would be doubled back on itself.

The nomads' mobility encouraged cross-currents of influence and the transmission of a uniform style over enormous areas. Metalwork of essentially the same spirit is found all the way from eastern Europe to Mongolia, although artists of each region had favourite designs which set their work apart. In the 'tears' at the roots of this animal's wings and the circle flanked by 'floppy triangles' on its haunches we can see the tell-tale signatures of Central Asian craftsmanship. The essence of the Animal Style, common to all regions, lay in its imaginative stylization of animal forms for decorative effect. Less elegant and refined than contemporary Achaemenid art, it more than compensates with a greater boldness and exuberance. Here the various elements of the composite animal are still readily recognizable, but in many works stylization is pursued to far greater lengths, reducing the animal to a series of rounded geometrical forms which pass at a glance for purely abstract designs.

The nomads' main source of raw material was the 'griffin gold' — so named after the fierce beasts which were said to watch over it — of the Altai Mountains in Siberia. The round cavities on this monster's haunches and shoulder were originally inlaid with stone. Turquoise, one of the few coloured stones available in the steppes, was a favourite material for this purpose.

The best known of the steppe nomads are the Scythians who, in Herodotus' day, occupied the lands north of the Black Sea. They probably spoke an Indo-Iranian language belonging to the same general family as English and most other western European languages. Later Classical authors also class as Scythian the tribes north of Iran and Afghanistan. Extending this usage, many modern writers now apply a Scythian label to all Animal-Style art as far east as Mongolia, but this obscures what must have been a great diversity of tribal and ethnic groups. Herodotus himself distinguishes many different Scythian and other nomadic tribes. As always, he throws some interesting if unreliable light on their customs and habits. The Massagetae women, he tells us with horror, though each married to one man, were 'used promiscuously'. 'If a man wants a woman, all he does is hang up his quiver in front of her wagon and then enjoy her without misgiving.' And old men were disposed of by being ritually slain, boiled up and eaten by their relatives! Little wonder that Herodotus 'the father of history' has also been called the 'father of lies'.

The greatest collection of Scythian art was amassed by the Russian Tsar Peter the Great in the early eighteenth century. Since those finds came from burial mounds which were not excavated scientifically, dating of this material still involves a possible error of some centuries. For the Oxus head-dress ornament, stylistic comparisons offer little help in narrowing the timespan suggested by the other finds in that great treasure — the fifth to second centuries BC. A date towards the middle of this range is perhaps the most likely.

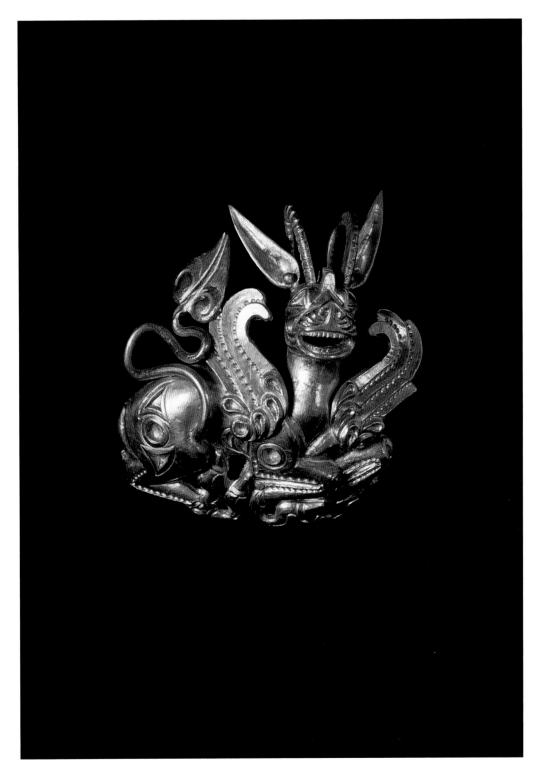

The Land of the Pharaohs: Egypt

By their practice of keeping records, the Egyptians have made themselves much the most learned of any people of which I have had experience ... More monuments which beggar description are to be found there than anywhere else in the world.
Herodotus

To a Greek like Herodotus, journeying through the East in the fifth century BC, Egypt was the grand civilization *par excellence*. An exotic world of mystery, splendour and unrivalled grandeur, the land of the pharaohs towered above the Mediterranean like a colossus. The Egyptian priests possessed a vast body of sacred knowledge, by which Herodotus was clearly impressed if not always convinced; they could recount the deeds of kings beyond even the dimmest memories of Greek bards; and the pharaonic monuments dwarfed the constructions of other Mediterranean lands as if the work of children.

Herodotus called Egypt 'the gift of the Nile', and the river was indeed the lifeblood of the country, both defining the limits of cultivation and settlement, and serving as the chief means of internal transportation. Properly controlled, the annual floodwaters produced enormous agricultural yields; in Classical times, the narrow ribbon of green along its banks served as the bread-basket of the Mediterranean. Most other requirements of urban life — metals, stones and so on — were readily available along the Nile valley or in the neighbouring deserts.

Remote from the major urban civilizations of the Near East, Egypt regarded the surrounding semi-nomads and other less sophisticated peoples with contempt: the 'wretched Asiatics', the 'vile Libyans' and the 'primitive Nubians'. Geography and demography thus conspired to encourage in the Egyptians an inward-looking and self-sustaining culture, for which stability — the maintenance of the established order — was the ultimate virtue. The basic religious, political and cultural framework of Egyptian life took shape soon after the foundation of the First Dynasty (c.3000 BC), and the outward forms remained essentially unchanged for millennia thereafter. This is manifested most clearly in the extraordinary continuity of Egyptian art. Buildings, statues and writings that are separated in time further than we are from Christ can be almost identical. With very rare exceptions — notably in the 'Amarna Revolution' — innovation and change injected only minor variations into a theme of striking continuity.

The unification of 'Upper' (southern) and 'Lower' (northern) Egypt around 3000 BC was the political manifestation of a great cultural transformation during the late Predynastic Period, which saw also a burgeoning of the arts and the invention of hieroglyphic writing (cat. nos 2, 19). The duality of the 'Two Lands', united in the person of the pharaoh, remained a permanent fixture of Egyptian ideology, even in times of strong central government. Only through the agency of the god-king was the political and spiritual unity of the land maintained. He wore both a 'White Crown' of Upper Egypt and a 'Red Crown' of Lower Egypt, as well as a 'Double Crown' combining the two. Each region had its patron deity — the vulture-goddess Nekhbet for the south, the cobra-goddess Wadjit for the north. Side by side on the pharaoh's brow, the symbols of these gods became the pre-eminent emblem of Egyptian kingship.

The dynastic divisions of Egyptian history were the work of an historian–priest of the third century BC; the Egyptians themselves simply recorded each king in succession. Modern scholars group these dynasties into three kingdoms — an Old, Middle and New — representing periods of strength and unity. These kingdoms were each followed by Intermediate Periods, marking episodes of political turmoil and foreign domination. An Archaic and a Late Period round off the beginning and end of the dynastic sequence.

Among the earliest inscriptions of the first dynasties are references to military campaigns south into Nubia and east across the desert, probably to Palestine. Ambitious kings ever after were obliged to wage war on these same widely separated fronts. The aim in both cases was chiefly to control valuable trade-routes and resources, especially Nubia's rich gold-fields. Occasionally, in times of weakness, the tables were turned and the Asiatics or Nubians would overrun the Nile valley.

The first few dynasties also witnessed the formation of the fundamental canons of Egyptian art, the basic motifs, conventions and themes which were to characterize art in the land of pharaohs for three millennia: the anatomy-defying combination of profile heads and frontal shoulders; the pharaoh with uplifted mace symbolically smiting his enemies; and, running through it all, the distinctive Egyptian talent for elegantly stylizing natural forms.

A crucial point was the reign of Djoser (c.2630–2611 BC), whose tomb is the first truly monumental Egyptian structure — the step pyramid at Saqqara. Even this was soon dwarfed by the flat-sided pyramids of the Fourth Dynasty kings at Giza. These gargantuan constructions indicate a despotic control of national resources and a single-minded concern with royal prestige that have few ancient or modern parallels. Royal conceit seems to have slackened somewhat in the following dynasty, when high offices, previously reserved for the king's family, were opened up to the nobility. The increased prestige of these prominent local families is reflected in their more imposing tombs and funerary images (cat. nos 20, 21).

Increasing independence of the regional governors led to the breakdown of central power in the First Intermediate Period (2134–2040 BC), a time of famine and weakness when rival dynasties were established at Thebes and Heracleopolis. It was the northern Heracleopolitan dynasty which reunited the country, marking the foundation of the Middle Kingdom (2040–1640 BC). Basing itself on Old Kingdom guidelines, the early art and literature of the Twelfth Dynasty was itself later taken as a model of perfection. Royal portraits of the time show a new emphasis on character, graphically rendering the pharaoh's care-worn features, as if to emphasize the burdens and responsibilities of leadership.

The many short-lived reigns of the

Egypt

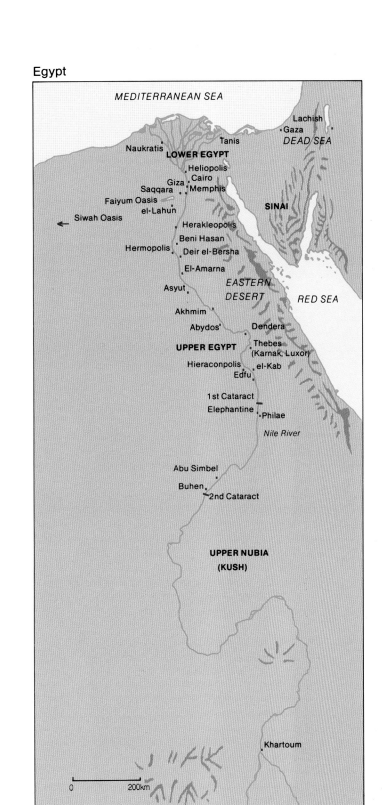

MEDITERRANEAN SEA

Lachish
Gaza
DEAD SEA
Tanis
Naukratis
LOWER EGYPT
Heliopolis
Cairo
Giza
Memphis
Saqqara
SINAI
Faiyum Oasis
el-Lahun
← Siwah Oasis
Herakleopolis
Beni Hasan
Hermopolis
Deir el-Bersha
El-Amarna
EASTERN
DESERT
Asyut
RED SEA
Akhmim
Abydos
Dendera
UPPER EGYPT
Thebes
(Karnak, Luxor)
Hieraconpolis
el-Kab
Edfu
1st Cataract
Elephantine
Philae
Nile River

Abu Simbel
Buhen
2nd Cataract

UPPER NUBIA
(KUSH)

Khartoum

0   200km

Thirteenth Dynasty saw power devolve increasingly to the king's viziers, leaving the country weakened and unable to repel the hordes of Hyksos — literally 'rulers of foreign lands' — who infiltrated from Syro-Palestine at this time. In the Second Intermediate Period (1640–1550 BC), these Asiatics over-ran much of the country, and for a century ruled over its northern districts.

The expulsion of the Hyksos by Ahmose, founder of the Eighteenth Dynasty, signalled the beginning of Egypt's most glorious and powerful period — the New Kingdom (1550–1070 BC). Conquerors like Tuthmosis I, Tuthmosis III and Ramesses II campaigned further than ever before, marching deep into Nubia and Syria. Palestine was firmly held and garrisoned, but for Syria the Egyptians had to vie by arms and diplomacy (which included taking foreign princesses into the royal harem) with two other great powers: the Hittites of Anatolia and the Kingdom of Mitanni, a Hurrian state which arose at this time in Syro-Mesopotamia. Relations with more distant Babylonia (now ruled by the Kassites) could be more cordial. Letters from Amarna record how the 'brothers' exchanged gifts, and complained if these did not live up to expectation!

The wealth of the New Kingdom is reflected in its lavish court life and spectacular monuments, the most imposing of any since the pyramids. The state capital Thebes received special attention, particularly the temples of the state god Amun-Re at Karnak and Luxor, still the high-points of a Theban tour today.

The familiar names are also mostly from this period, indeed from two generations of the fourteenth century BC: the physically deformed pharaoh Akhenaten (1353–1335 BC) who caused a religious upheaval by supressing all other gods in favour of the sun-disc Aten; his beautiful wife Nefertiti; and the boy-king who succeeded a few years after him, Tutankhamun. King Tut's short and historically insignificant reign (1333–1323 BC) has been thrown out of all proportion by the discovery of his unrobbed tomb in 1922. Many other kings would have had much richer burials, but sadly they have all long since been plundered.

The prestige and authority of the Theban priests of Amun-Re increased greatly during the New Kingdom, and in the succeeding Third Intermediate Period (1070–712 BC) the high-priest ruled Upper Egypt virtually as a separate state, sometimes even adopting royal titles. Most of the coffins and the mummy in the exhibition are from the numerous burials of the large Theban priest-hood of these times, which — unusually for Egypt — gave women a prominent role (cat. nos 38–40).

Egypt fragmented further under the Twenty-second Dynasty, so that by 712 BC there were four 'kings' ruling simultaneously. One was a Nubian whose dynasty had entered the mêlée from the south fifty years earlier, and it was he who eventually re-stored to Egypt some semblance of unity and international standing. The Nubian conquest marks the beginning of the Late Period (712–332 BC). As if wishing to appear more Egyptian than the Egyptians, the Nubians of the Twenty-fifth Dynasty proceeded to revive many old traditions that had been allowed to lapse. A vigorous cultural renaissance saw more new monuments erected in fifty years than in the previous two centuries, many in consciously old-fashioned styles (cat. no. 43).

If it was foreigners who restored Egypt to a position of greatness, it was foreigners also who soon destroyed her independence entirely, absorbing the country into a succession of mighty Near Eastern empires. A brief Assyrian conquest (c.671–655 BC) was followed by clashes with Babylon and then the more lasting dominations of the Persians (the Twenty-seventh and Thirty-first Dynasties). Greeks were often used as mercenaries in these centuries and some had settled in Egypt. The next great conqueror, Alexander the Great (334–323 BC), opened the gates to full Greek rule under the Ptolemies, leading to a superficial synthesis of Greek and Egyptian culture. Alexandria, the city he founded on the Mediterranean coast (and his own final resting place), was to become one of the foremost economic and cultural centres of the world, renowned especially for its enormous library.

Queen Cleopatra, perhaps today the most famous of all ancient Egyptians, was the last of the Ptolemaic line. With her suicide in 30 BC, Egypt passed into the Roman Empire under Augustus' direct control; such was the country's strategic importance that he and later emperors insisted on ruling Egypt personally through a prefect. Native culture was little affected by the veneer of Greco-Roman ways; the last known hieroglyphic inscription was not carved until AD 394. The following year saw the split of the Roman Empire into East and West, a symptom of the schism that the adoption of Christianity had brought to the unwieldy Roman domain. It was the advent of this new and exclusive religion — a faith less tolerant of polytheism than other pagan religions had been — which finally brought about the demise and disintegration of pharaonic Egyptian culture.

Writing in the fifth century BC, Herodotus remarked that the Egyptians 'are religious to excess, beyond any other nation in the world'. Modern research has only served to confirm this judgement, showing how thoroughly the Egyptian world view and the conduct of their daily lives was imbued with a consciousness of the gods. As in Mesopotamia, deities personified a wide range of natural features, physical and supernatural forces, abstract concepts, skills and so on. The pharaoh, too, was a god — the son of Re and the embodiment of falcon-headed Horus while he lived, transmuted at death into the Lord of the Dead, Osiris. And strangest of all to Herodotus, even animals were seen as physical manifestations of divinities, revered in life and mummified in death (cat. no. 50). Most deities were themselves depicted with the head — sometimes the whole body — of an animal (cat. nos 32, 47, 48, 51).

The pyramids and mummies that dominate the popular image of ancient Egypt today easily leave the impression of a people obsessed with death. The Egyptians did indeed take enormous trouble over the proper treatment of the dead, disembowelling and anointing the body, wrapping it in linen and, for the rich, burying it in an elaborate tomb accompanied by all the finery of life. This process was not, however, a celebration of death, but rather a necessary preparation for rebirth in the next life. The Egyptians believed it essential that the physical remains survive, for once the soul had been judged deserving before Osiris (cat. no. 32) it would once again use the body as its principal abode, and the mummy would live and breathe again. Indeed, the climax of the funerary ceremony performed on the mummy at the cemetery was called the Opening of the Mouth.

Egyptian public art was exclusively religious, whether destined for a temple, palace or any other state monument. Glorification of the pharaoh — the living link between heaven and earth — went hand in hand with the celebration of the gods who nurtured and sustained him. Private funerary reliefs, too, had a sacred purpose, though the scenes are often drawn from everyday life (cat. no. 22). The distinctive conventions of Egyptian painting and relief sculpture were the same in both. Lacking any understanding of perspective or foreshortening (both essentially Greek discoveries), the picture plane was treated not as a three-dimensional space but as a neutral element which in no way determined what was shown. How much of an object was drawn was decided not by what could be seen from any one viewpoint but by what information needed to be conveyed. Like Egyptian hieroglyphs, these artistic images are codes which often have to be deciphered to be properly understood.

Although the Egyptian language bears a distant relation to the Semitic tongues of the Near East, the Egyptians regarded themselves as decidedly different, and their culture is indeed distinctive and self-centred in a way no Near Eastern society could claim. Egyptian art, emphatically unconditioned by outside forces, remained always unmistakably Egyptian. Occasional borrowings from abroad did occur — notably from early Sumer (cat. no. 19), and from Bronze-Age and Hellenistic Greece — but these were always incidental to what was essentially a self-sustaining tradition. The native Egyptian genius alone is responsible for one of the most truly individual and profoundly successful episodes in the history of art.

The Battlefield Palette

Egyptian ceremonial palette
c.3100 BC (Late Predynastic Period)
Egypt (Abydos?)
slate
32.8 cm height
cat. no. 19

The distinctive conventions and iconography of Egyptian art emerged very quickly during the first few dynasties (c.3000–2800 BC) and remained remarkably consistent for thousands of years thereafter. This makes Egyptian artefacts and monuments the most easy to recognize of any from antiquity, for the layman no less than for the trained specialist. The battlefield scene on this ceremonial palette, however, bears few of the usual Egyptian hallmarks: the inelegantly plump, contorted figures are arranged chaotically all over the field; they flagrantly disobey the shoulders-frontal rule (see cat. no. 22); and the scene as a whole has none of the concern for decorative elegance which is the guiding spirit of the canonical Egyptian style.

Even in later periods, illustrations of warfare and destruction were often treated differently to other scenes, the chaos and confusion of battle being graphically mirrored in the ill-ordered distribution of twisted figures up and down the picture-plane. A few centuries later we would expect to see the king, represented larger than the other figures and in a more conventional style, triumphantly leading the assault. This palette, however, was made too early for such a composition to have been conceived. It belongs to the brief period of a century or two before the founding of the First Dynasty, when the new interests of Egyptian craftsmen were leading them beyond utilitarian objects and small trinket carvings to larger and more ambitious works, but before the standard style we know as Egyptian had crystallized. Many of these objects are now found concentrated in temples rather than graves. It was a period of much innovation and experimentation, partly inspired, it seems, by contact with the arts of Sumer and Elam (Persia). Around this time, Sumerian artefacts such as cylinder seals began to appear in Egypt, and Sumerian and Elamite motifs and building practices were copied by Egyptian craftsmen and architects. The impact was shortlived: Eastern imports disappeared in the first few dynasties, and the borrowed motifs were soon transformed by the Egyptians' rapidly evolving sense of design. Brief though it was, however, Mesopotamian influence came at a crucial time and played its part in the emergence of a distinctive Egyptian style.

This palette lacks the most conspicuously Mesopotamian features of some contemporary works. The man in a long robe at top right, and the chaotic, almost aerial scattering of figures all over the picture-plane have been seen as vestiges of Sumerian influence, but both features could equally well have local origins (the robe in Libya). The scene of animals flanking a palm-tree on the reverse of the palette is formally close to a common Sumerian motif of goats on either side of a tree; but the species of beasts represented here — giraffes, long-necked gazelles or some mythological hybrid — and the decoratively stylized forms in which they are cast are quite alien to Sumer. Indeed, this elegant, symmetrical composition is the most Egyptian-looking aspect of the palette; the Sumerian motif — if such it was — has already been thoroughly adapted. The bird which looks on is a variety of guinea fowl.

The battlefield scene is laden with symbolism but its meaning now largely escapes us. Does the scene portray a particular event or a generalized picture of military mayhem? It is impossible to say. Are the naked victims of the carnage — bound with their arms behind their backs and preyed upon by vultures and ravens — Egyptians or foreigners? Here at least we are on firmer ground, for Egyptians usually do not have beards; the curly hair of these men suggests Nubians from the south (Sudan or Ethiopia). Two at the top left are marched along by bird-topped 'standards' or ensigns, symbolically provided with arms for grasping their prisoners. The long-robed figure leads one of their number to a lion, which is busy devouring the contorted body of another victim. In later periods the lion frequently symbolizes the pharaoh (cat. no. 30), and here too it may represent the king engaged in one of the battles which led to the unification of Egypt around 3000 BC. According to Egyptian tradition, the First Dynasty was founded when Menes, a leader of Upper Egypt, conquered Lower Egypt and thereby united the 'Two Lands'.

The semi-circle at the top (approximately the middle of the complete palette) is part of a central cavity in which colourful minerals were supposedly ground to make eye-paint. Remains of blue-green malachite and red haematite have been found on the plain and animal-shaped slate palettes from burials of this time. Large decorated palettes like this, however, were probably never used for this purpose; they are found in temples, where they were apparently presented as offerings to the gods.

The upper fragment is a cast of the original, now in the Ashmolean Museum, Oxford.

cat. no. **19**

Egyptian noblewoman

Funerary statuette
c.2400 BC, 4th or 5th Dynasty (Old Kingdom)
Egypt, findspot unknown
alabaster
48.7 cm height
cat. no. 20

Clarity, formalism and elegance — this small statue of a noblewoman has all the quintessential characteristics of Egyptian art. It is a work of the Old Kingdom, dating to the time of the great pyramids at Giza. This was a crucial period in the development of Egyptian art, when many standard motifs and themes were given their classic expressions. The restrained elegance and avoidance of unnecessary detail, which are the hallmarks of the period, have much in common with the spirit of early Classical Greek art, though without the same interest in naturalism. And, as in the case of Classical Greece, later generations of Egyptian artists would repeatedly return to this 'Severe Style' for models of stylistic perfection. It is Egyptian art at its purest — austere and unadorned.

A sculpture of such fine quality was almost certainly carved in a royal workshop, and its subject must have been a woman of some status — the wife of a high official if not a member of the royal family itself. The simple pose and dress, the fleshy face and the heavy wig are all standard features of statuettes of Old Kingdom royal women. Her striated wig and parted hair (just revealed at the forehead) provide the only elements of patterning on the otherwise smooth surfaces of clothes and flesh, which merge into one another without any clear indication of where one begins and the other ends. The simple, long garment follows closely the contours of the woman's body, which is simplified without being conspicuously stylized. The subtle modelling of the fleshy stomach and the exquisite detailing of face, hands and wig indicate the hand of a skilled sculptor trained in the best tradition of the classical Old Kingdom style.

The statuette is a funerary image which would have stood in the woman's tomb — or that of her husband — providing a substitute home for her ka-soul, released from her body at death. During the Fifth Dynasty, high administrative posts, previously reserved for the pharaoh's immediate family, were opened up also to favoured nobles. Many of these non-royal administrators built grand tombs which they stocked with fine sculptures of themselves and their families. Like the example here, most by this time tended to be rather less than life-size.

The statuette was originally painted. There are traces of black on the wig and green (now turned to brown) on the back of the dress. Convention required women's flesh to be lighter than that of men — a suntan was the sign of an outdoor labourer. This was indicated by painting women's flesh areas in yellow, and men's in red.

The priest Tjeti

Funerary statuette
c.2300–2100 BC, 6th Dynasty (Old Kingdom) or
1st Intermediate Period
Akhmim, Egypt
painted wood; eyes inlaid with copper, limestone
and obsidian
75.5 cm height
cat. no. 21

Once locked away in its owner's tomb, this statuette of the priest Tjeti was never again supposed to be seen by human eyes. Its purpose was to provide a home for the dead man's *ka*, which was released from his body, along with various other spirits, at death. While we may judge it as art, and see in it some expression of Egyptian aesthetic principles, for the man who commissioned it the success of the statue had little to do with any considerations of beauty or likeness to his actual features, and everything to do with the survival of his spirit after death.

In the period after the great pyramids of the Fourth Dynasty, the right to an elaborate burial spread from the king and his family to a wider circle of noble courtiers and officials. In the First Dynasty, the graves around the king's tomb were simple pits with very few offerings. But as the pharaohs built larger tombs, and eventually pyramids, the officials' burials grew also. In the Sixth Dynasty, when this statue was probably made, they generally consisted of an underground burial chamber entered by a shaft and covered by a rectangular brick or stone structure known as a *mastaba*, the Arabic term for bench. Next to the *mastaba* chapel, where food offerings would be placed, was a sealed room (*serdab*) containing a statue of the deceased. Sometimes a number of statues showed the tomb owner at different ages. This youthful-looking Tjeti was probably not the only statue included in his burial — two other uninscribed sculptures have been plausibly identified as representing him. The funerary statue(s) served both as a substitute 'body' for the deceased's *ka*-spirit and as a focal point for cult offerings. The dead man's after-life depended on the continuing survival of his *ka* and its ability to leave the burial chamber for offerings of food. Slits in the *serdab* wall allowed the statue to gaze out into the offering chapel and the food to pass through in the other direction. Before it was sealed up at burial, a ceremony known as the Opening of the Mouth would be enacted on the statue to endow it with the senses of speech, sight and hearing, and thus prepare it for the deceased's rebirth. In later periods, when embalming was no longer a privilege of the king and his immediate family, the mummy came to be regarded as the *ka*'s principal home and the Opening of the Mouth would be performed on it also (see cat. no. 40, right side).

The formal conventions of Egyptian art never allowed any real sense of movement. Tjeti is supposed to be striding forward, and at first glance he is; but the traditional distribution of weight evenly on both legs and the firm planting of both feet flat on the ground renders him immobile. This is not the stance of a real walker but of a stationary person who has slid one foot forward. The staff of office in Tjeti's left hand is a modern replacement, the original having been lost. He also held something in his right hand, probably a short baton or roll of linen.

Men (but not women) were increasingly shown naked in the funerary statues as the Old Kingdom progressed, though some Sixth-Dynasty figures still wear a loin-cloth. The soft modelling of Tjeti's stomach and legs is observant and well executed, but the naturalism is otherwise superficial. The taste for elegant, elongated forms — imposed also by the relatively narrow logs used for carving — results in over-long limbs, an unnaturally thin waist and a narrow torso. The arms were carved separately (the left one in two pieces) and attached by mortise and tenon.

The eyes are inlaid with white crystalline limestone and black obsidian (a volcanic glass) in copper eyelids. The nipples are inlaid in wood.

The whole statue was originally painted; clear traces survive, especially around the shoulders and head. Flesh areas are coloured in the conventional sun-tanned ruddy-brown. The hair and nipples are painted black. Tjeti's thick, short wig, falling in multiple tiers of small tresses from the level of the forehead, was popular around the end of the Sixth Dynasty. In many periods, both men and women cut their hair short and wore wigs.

The inscription on the base gives Tjeti's titles as 'Treasurer of the King of Lower Egypt, sole friend, lector priest, staff [i.e. support] of the Apis-bull, controller of the bird trap, overseer of priests, master of secrets, one honoured by the Great God, Tjeti'. This elaborate identification was part of the process which earmarked the statue for the soul of its prospective occupant, ensuring that Tjeti alone could use it.

cat. no. 21

Egyptian noblewoman

Painted relief
*c.*1890–1860 BC, 12th Dynasty (Middle Kingdom)
from the tomb of Djehutihotep, Deir el-Bersha,
Egypt
painted plaster on limestone
71.0 x 34.0 cm

cat. no. 22

The unmistakable signature of Egyptian art is its peculiar way of representing the human form in paintings and relief sculpture. Rather than a single consistent view, the artist attempts to show us a combination of various different views welded together. This presents no real difficulty with subjects as familiar as human figures, but Egyptian representations of less common objects can be much harder to read.

This figure is from the tomb of the Twelfth Dynasty governor Djehutihotep and shows one of his sisters. She is elaborately be-jewelled and wears a long, plain white dress and a hair band. Her skin is the conventional yellow which signifies a privileged life shaded from the hot Egyptian sun.

Images were not just pictures to the Egyptians, they had a life and powers of their own. This extended even to the images used in writing, giving rise to the strange practice of 'mutilated hieroglyphs': to prevent any of the beings represented in funerary inscriptions on coffins and tombs from coming to life and harming the deceased, these texts were written with incomplete or 'mutilated' signs. Snakes are cut in half; scorpions have no stings; animals and birds lack legs; humans are just heads and arms. Thus mutilated, no evil forces would be able to threaten anyone!

Normal pictures, on the other hand, attempted to show as much as possible of an object, even if this was not completely visible from a single viewpoint. Pictures of people particularly had to show all their essential components — head, chest, legs and so on. But the simplest and most natural way to depict each of these was not always the same. Since the relations between figures, and the direction of movement, ran along (rather than out of) the picture plane, heads had to be shown in profile (though they are given frontal eyes), and this was also the easiest way to represent legs and feet. But the torso would have been largely lost in a profile view, which anyway required a greater understanding of foreshortening than the Egyptians had achieved. So to picture the upper body they ignored anatomical constraints and turned the shoulders round to face the viewer a full ninety degrees from the line of the head. When clothes were shown, as in this relief, these also were represented as if seen front-on. The profile of the torso itself is a compromise between this impossible combination: the line from the front armpit to the waist attempts to show a profile of the chest running through the nipple; the rear profile is an almost straight connecting line.

Treating all of the front torso line as a chest profile worked tolerably well on men but made nonsense of women's breasts. Dresses like those worn by Djehutihotep's sister in fact covered the breasts, but the profile treatment forced artists to show the left breast shifted sideways and exposed. Long hair also becomes problematic: should it be shown falling both sides of the neck onto the frontal shoulders? Or only on the one visible side of the profile head and neck? Egyptian art opted for the latter. Again in defiance of anatomy, both feet were shown as if seen from the inside, so that only the big toe is drawn.

Strange and misleading as it was, this code for showing the human form lasted virtually unchanged for the entire course of pharaonic history, a period of more than 3000 years.

cat. no. 22

Menkheperresoneb, priest of Amun

Seated statue
*c.*1450 BC, 18th Dynasty (New Kingdom)
Thebes, Egypt
granite
81.2 cm height
cat. no. 23

With the reunification of Egypt in about 1550 BC under a dynasty ruling from Thebes, the city's god Amun — by this time merged with the sun-god to form Amun-Re — took on the status of state deity. The New Kingdom priests of Amun thus came to enjoy unprecedented power and influence, some high-priests of the Twenty-first Dynasty even claiming royal status.

The high-priest of Amun under Tuthmosis III and Amenophis II — one of the most glorious eras in Egyptian history — was Menkheperresoneb, the man portrayed in this statue. As the grandson of a royal wetnurse, Menkheperresoneb was brought up in the palace, where he would have come to know the king from an early age. His name means 'may Menkheperre [Tuthmosis III] prosper', and was surely bestowed as a mark of royal favour. Despite his claim to have been 'picked out for his qualities', this friendship clearly played a major role in Menkheperresoneb's meteoric rise. He was, as his tomb inscriptions relate,

> the one whom his lord advanced in the midst of the Royal Companions and chose from among the people, whom the king of Upper Egypt made great while he was (yet) a weaned child and whose position in the palace he advanced.

He became a 'divine father' and 'second priest of Amun' without going through any of the usual lesser positions, and was eventually promoted to 'first priest of Amun', that is, the high-priest of all the Egyptian clergy. This was one of the most powerful offices in the land, and Menkheperresoneb's duties included supervising many of the royal building projects and workshops, and receiving for Amun's temple the rich tribute of the foreign lands intimidated by Tuthmosis III's many conquests. His tomb reliefs show the high-priest receiving offerings from as far as Crete (Kheftiu), Anatolia (Kheta), and the Sudan (Kush).

Egyptian sculpture relied upon a very limited number of standard types, and this classic seated pose was one of the most enduring; throughout the 3000 years of pharaonic history only the dress and placement of the hands change significantly. Menkheperresoneb places one hand reverentially to his chest and holds a piece of folded linen — a common symbol of high office — in the other. A long, plain robe follows the basic contours of his body but — the artist being unconcerned with the subtleties of anatomy — bulges too high at the chest.

The sculptor has kept elaboration to a bare minimum. All the surfaces are smooth and flat, even the usually textured wig, though some detailing may originally have been added in paint. The sleeves and collar are invisible, so smoothly do the exposed and robed areas blend into one another.

The statue is almost totally undamaged, the face preserving a perfect image of the loyal and conscientious servant. Despite his high office, Menkheperresoneb's expression and gesture bespeak nothing but humility; in Egyptian art it is generally only the pharaoh who affects real power and self-importance.

The inscriptions on this statue describe Menkheperresoneb merely as 'seal-bearer of the king and second priest of Amun', indicating that it was made relatively early in his career, probably soon after the death of Hatshepsut left Tuthmosis III as sole occupant of the throne (1458 BC). In the front inscription he is called 'the blessed one before Amun in Karnak', the Theban temple in which this statue was probably set up. The texts on the sides are invocations to Amun and Re-Harakhti for funerary offerings to be made to his spirit after death. The occurrences of Amun's name were erased during the reign of Akhenaten, the heretic who suppressed all gods other than the sun-disc Aten, but they were re-inscribed soon after, when Amun and his priesthood were restored.

cat. no. 23

Head of Amenophis III

From a colossal statue of the pharaoh
1391–1353 BC, 18th Dynasty (New Kingdom)
from the mortuary temple of Amenophis III,
Thebes, Egypt
quartzite
1.17 m height
cat. no. 24

This colossal head, weighing almost one and a half tonnes, is all that remains of an enormous statue of Amenophis III from his mortuary temple near the Valley of the Kings at Thebes. One of an identical pair, each carved from a single block of stone, the full height of the seated figure (standing statues of this size are less common) would have been some eight metres. Not without justification did Amenophis boast that his statues were 'higher than the rising of the heavens; their rays are in men's faces like the rising sun'. Made of 'granite, of quartzite and of precious stones, they were fashioned to last forever'. But later kings had other ideas. Amenophis' 'everlasting fortress', the most magnificent mortuary temple Egypt had ever seen, was ruthlessly pillaged by later pharaohs for its stone and precious fittings. The rest of this colossal figure probably ended up as building blocks.

The Egyptians were the supreme masters of scale, exploiting more effectively than any other ancient civilization the dramatic impact of sheer size. Grandiose buildings and statues naturally came to be seen as manifestations of the pharaoh's power and authority, and it is therefore no accident that nearly all the largest sculptures were carved during the New Kingdom, when Egyptian power was at its height. Two pharaohs in particular were responsible for most of the colossal statues of that era: Ramesses II (Nineteenth Dynasty) and Amenophis III, the subject of this piece.

Unlike Ramesses, Amenophis was not a great conqueror. In thirty-eight years of rule (1391–1353 BC), he led only one military expedition, preferring to take foreign princesses into his harem than confront their fathers on the battlefield. In the reigns of his successors this limp foreign policy began to come unstuck, but Amenophis had the good fortune to come to the throne after a series of able leaders had secured the largest empire Egypt had known and had enriched the treasuries beyond all imaginings. Much of this great wealth was spent in lavish building programs, particularly in the capital Thebes, where the magnificent Luxor Temple, boasting the tallest colonnade in all Egypt, was largely his work. Amenophis' mortuary temple on the opposite bank of the river was no less impressive. In his own words, it was 'a very great monument ... without equal since the beginning of time ... wrought with gold throughout, its floors adorned with silver and all its portals with fine gold'.

This head shows Amenophis wearing the Red Crown of Lower Egypt. The top of the crown has been broken off; what we see is the lower, cylindrical part, which originally rose up steeply at the back. A cobra, the pre-eminent Egyptian symbol of kingship, meanders down the front and rears up over the king's brow. The narrow strap extending from his temples around to the damaged chin was worn by the pharaoh for attaching the false beard (here broken away), another symbol of royalty.

As the incarnation of Horus, the pharaoh was a living god, and his portraits show it. Serene, all-powerful and confident, Amenophis' face presents the Egyptian stereotype of divine kingship. This was by then a standard formula that changed only slightly from reign to reign (with the notable exception of Amenophis' son, the 'monotheistic' heretic Akhenaten). There is no trace of individuality, no hint of personality, in his striking but bland visage. It is kingship personified — which is to say that it is not a person at all.

The elegantly fluid lines and smooth surfaces are oblivious to the irregularities and blemishes of real life. Facial features are reduced to their purest and simplest forms, sharpened up at critical points to accentuate the definition of this minimalist image. While remaining faithful to the overall forms of nature, the artist exploits to the full the abrupt transitions and the shadows cast by the lips, giving them unnaturally sharp outer edges and dwelling on the smooth transitions at the corners of the mouth, where we detect the hint of a benevolent smile.

The carving is technically flawless and still retains the lustre of its final polishing. Roughly shaped by the age-old method of pounding with tools of stone (probably dolerite and silex), the head was polished using quartzite and sand abrasive. Although the Egyptians usually painted their sculptures so that the type of stone could not be seen, important works tended to be carved in very hard stones which would — or so they hoped — last forever. The quartzite used for this statue had to be shipped up-river, over 500 kilometres from the 'Red Mountain' near Cairo.

This head, together with its matching pair and other smaller statues of Amenophis from his mortuary temple, was bought by the British Museum in 1823 from Henry Salt, the British Consul-General in Egypt. At considerable personal expense Salt acquired most of the large Egyptian sculptures now in the Museum, though he was never adequately reimbursed; such was the enthusiasm for Greek sculpture caused by the arrival of the Elgin marbles from Athens that all other ancient art was regarded as second-rate.

Colossal head of Amenophis III *in situ* at his mortuary temple, Thebes. (The head pictured is the partner to the head displayed.) In the background are two seated statues of the King (the so-called 'Colossi of Memnon'). These are virtually the only standing remains of this once magnificent temple.

cat. no. 24

Head of a pharaoh

Amenophis III or Ramesses II
c.1390–1225 BC, 18th or 19th Dynasty
(New Kingdom)
Thebes, Egypt
quartzite
22.0 cm height
cat. no. 25

The conventional stylization of facial features in most Egyptian royal portraiture makes the identification of individual rulers extremely difficult. Unless an inscription giving the subject's name is preserved, there is often no sure way of telling the statue of one pharaoh from another, for each presents the world with much the same stereotyped visage of perfect features, and the same expression of benevolent serenity. It was a measure of the scant regard for actual likeness that even women could be reduced to this character-shielding, idealized form, as when Queen Hatshepsut succeeded her husband on the throne (1473–1458 BC) and, in an effort to make her rule more acceptable to the conservative priesthood and populace, had herself portrayed with the body and face of a man, even wearing the pharaonic false beard. In the case of some portrait heads, it is still not possible to say whether they are of Hatshepsut or of her nephew and eventual successor Tuthmosis III.

A similar uncertainty surrounds this head, which was long thought to represent Ramesses II (1290–1224 BC), the great warrior king of the Nineteenth Dynasty. Some inscribed statues show that king looking much like this, and wearing the same oddly-shaped war helmet. But most scholars now identify this piece as Amenophis III, the subject of the colossal head (cat. no. 24) which is carved from the same type of stone. The more mask-like treatment of the face in this slightly under life-size head reflects a different stylistic model — the almond-shaped eyes rise slightly towards the sides of the face, and the mouth is much less full and curvaceous. But different schools or workshops, none of them much constrained by considerations of likeness, might easily have diverged this far and more in 'portraits' of one and the same king.

The Egyptian pharaoh was represented wearing a number of different crowns, each of which symbolized a different aspect of his kingship. The one on this head was a late addition to the series adopted in the Eighteenth Dynasty, and was worn by the king in battle. Called the Blue Crown (*khepresh*), blue being the most prestigious colour, it was covered with round gold ornaments, which can be seen on painted examples. At the front, like most other crowns, it bore a rearing cobra.

Royal head in idealizing style showing Queen Hatshepsut or King Tuthmosis III, c.1450 BC. (British Museum)

cat. no. **25**

The goddess Sekhmet

Seated statue
1391–1353 BC, 18th Dynasty (New Kingdom)
from the Temple of Mut, Thebes, Egypt
black granite
2.06 m height
cat. no. 26

The body of a woman, the head of a lioness; possessed of a ravenous bloodthirst; emanating a fiery glow and a scorching breath — such were the attributes of the fearsome goddess Sekhmet. The name means 'Mighty One', and that she certainly was. Fire, war and pestilence were her doing; the desiccating desert wind issued from her mouth; sickness and fever were the unwelcome gifts of her messengers; savage and vengeful, in the frenzy of her bloodlust she was unstoppable.

Sekhmet once tried to wipe out humanity entirely, and would have succeeded but for a mixture of beer-mash and red ochre which the sun-god Re had his high-priest prepare and pour over the landscape to look like the blood of her slain victims. Gorging herself on this cunning brew she became intoxicated and was unable to continue her bloodthirsty rampage.

But she was not always so hostile, or at least not to all men. Her destructive power was adopted by pharaohs as a symbol of their own invincible strength on the battlefield. She accompanied them to war, piercing the enemies' hearts with her arrows and scorching their bodies with her fiery breath. As the mistress of sickness, her magic was also the most powerful of cures. Sekhmet, 'great of magic' and 'lady of life', was invoked by priestly doctors in their prayers and treatments for the ill.

This statue is one of 365 identical figures of Sekhmet — one for every day of the year — set up by Amenophis III in the Temple of Mut in Thebes. A parallel series, showing the goddess standing and holding a papyrus-shaped sceptre, brought the total number of statues in the temple to 730. Amenophis evidently held her in special veneration, and more images of the goddess were placed in his mortuary temple. Altogether nearly 600 of these figures have been accounted for. Each day of the year a different statue in the Temple of Mut would be presented with food offerings for the goddess.

Sekhmet holds an *ankh* (life) symbol in her hand and is crowned by a solar disc of the sun-god Re, her father, and a royal *uraeus* (cobra), now broken away. The disc is carved from a separate piece of stone and mortised on. On the sides of the throne, papyrus and lily (?) flowers are entwined around the sign for unity (*sma*, originally a drawing of the lungs and windpipe), symbolizing the unification of Upper (lily) and Lower (papyrus) Egypt. The inscriptions on the front of the throne were added later by Sheshonq I (945–924 BC), whose names and titles they give. One of the last great Egyptian conquerors, Sheshonq is infamous from the Bible — where he is called Shishak — for invading Palestine and sacking Solomon's temple in Jerusalem.

Sekhmet was the wife of Ptah, chief god of the ancient capital of Memphis. The transfer of the royal residence to Thebes greatly increased the importance of the local triad there — Amun, Mut and Khons. Mut's prestige was enhanced by merging her identity with Sekhmet. This was not just sleight of hand: for the Egyptians a single deity could take on various different forms or aspects and this encouraged a very fluid notion of identity and separateness. As Amun became merged with the sun-god Re, Mut, his wife and 'eye', became leonine like Sekhmet and took on the war-goddess's fearsome character. The presence of so many statues of Sekhmet (Mut's name never occurs in the inscriptions) in a temple dedicated to Mut thus presented the Egyptians with no contradiction.

To the antiquarians of the eighteenth and nineteenth centuries, on the other hand, it presented an irresistible temptation. Serried ranks of these feline figures were then still partly exposed to view, and many of them were dug out and shipped off to Europe and America. The British Museum alone has some thirty examples, the largest collection outside Egypt. This piece came to the museum in 1823 along with much else assembled by the British Consul-General Henry Salt.

cat. no. 26

Egyptian jewellery

Bracelet
c.1400 B.C. (New Kingdom)
Egypt, findspot unknown
gold, lapis lazuli, cornelian and glazed
composition
20.0 cm length
cat. no. 27

Signet ring of the Pharaoh Akhenaten
1353–1335 BC, 18th Dynasty (New Kingdom)
Egypt, findspot unknown
gold
2.5 cm diameter
cat. no. 28

Funerary pectoral of the Lady Ptahemheb
c.1250 BC, 19th Dynasty (New Kingdom)
Egypt (Memphis?)
glazed composition ('faience')
12.3 x 12.7 cm
cat. no. 29

Ring of the Pharaoh Tuthmosis III
1479–1425 BC, 18th Dynasty (New Kingdom)
Egypt, findspot unknown
gold, blue glass
2.5 cm diameter
cat. no. 30

Necklace
c.1550–1300 BC (New Kingdom)
Egypt, findspot unknown
gold, cornelian and lapis lazuli
29.0 cm length
cat. no. 31

This selection of Egyptian jewellery all dates to the New Kingdom (1550–1070 BC), the period of Egypt's greatest conquests abroad and her most glorious monuments at home. The palace and temple treasuries had never been so rich, and a succession of able and industrious pharaohs spared no expense to ensure that their court life and burials were the most lavish and splendid the ancient world had ever seen. That the name of Tutankhamun is now a byword for fabulous wealth and opulence is due largely to the extraordinary amounts of jewellery that accompanied the young king to his tomb. And he, we should remember, was a relatively unimportant pharaoh. Yet his jewellery is surely among the most famous in the world today — a fact which serves as eloquent testimony to the enduring appeal of the Egyptians' supremely elegant and decorative jewellery designs.

As in all periods, the splendour of New Kingdom jewellery is based not on its stones — all of which we would class as semi-precious — but on its extravagant use of gold, which was obtained in the large goldfields of the Sudan (ancient Nubia). The Egyptian words for jeweller mean simply 'goldman' or 'gold craftsman'.

Some new forms appear at this time, including motifs from overseas, but by and large New Kingdom jewellery involves a more lavish treatment of traditional themes and designs. The bracelet (cat. no. 27) employs one of the Egyptians' favourite jewellery motifs, the scarab beetle, the symbol of the morning sun-god Khepri. This unlikely association arose from the beetle's habit of pushing a ball of dirt across the ground. The ball was likened to the sun-disc, which the scarab is often portrayed pushing up into the day. The analogy with the self-creating Khepri — 'he who is coming into being', as he was called — was reinforced by the fact that scarabs were seen to emerge, apparently spontaneously, from these balls. In fact, of course, they contain the beetle's eggs.

The gold ring (cat. no. 28), here illustrated sideways, is engraved with the name and titles of Akhenaten, the heretical pharaoh who suppressed the worship of all other gods in favour of the sun-disc Aten. The inscription gives his throne-name, Neferk-heprure waenre, and the epithet 'Praised by all Mankind'. The hieroglyph for 'mankind', a picture of a lapwing with its arms raised in worship, is set so that it adores the royal name in the centre of the ring. The name Akhenaten, by which the king is best known today, was adopted in place of his original birth-name to mark his conversion to exclusive Aten-worship. It means something like 'of service to the sun-disc'.

Stirrup-shaped signet-rings were a New Kingdom invention, and the larger examples like this were popular in the reign of Akhenaten. Paintings and reliefs show similar rings among the 'gold of honour' being cast down from a window by the generous pharaoh to favoured courtiers and officials. Those engraved with the royal name were probably seals of office, certifying the status of the holder and empowering him to act in the name of the king.

The gold and glass ring (cat. no. 30) also bears the name of a king: Tuthmosis III. Probably the greatest of all New Kingdom conquerors, Tuthmosis was responsible for bringing much of Syria and Palestine under Egyptian control. The ring consists of a rectangular blue glass plaque which swivels on the gold hoop so that either of its engraved faces can be displayed. The side shown here (again illustrated sideways) is inscribed with the king's 'Golden Horus' name: 'Mighty of Power' (Sekhempehti). The reverse bears a picture of the pharaoh as a man-headed sphinx, crushing a prostrate foe with his paw. Above, in a cartouche, is the king's throne-name, Menkheperre, and the title 'Good God, Conqueror of all Lands'.

Much of the Egyptian jewellery in museums today was not made to be worn in life at all, but to accompany the deceased to the grave. Numerous ornaments and amulets in the form of magical motifs were wrapped in the mummy's bindings. One crucial piece of equipment was the 'heart scarab', placed on the deceased's breast. This was sometimes incorporated into a rectangular pectoral (a large item of jewellery hung around the neck and worn over the chest), as in the item shown here (cat. no. 29). Shrine-shaped pectorals were a standard feature of any respectable Egyptian jewellery casket from the Middle Kingdom on. Royal pectorals and those intended for real life were often made of gold, but most funerary pectorals are made of so-called 'faience', an artificial glazed composition.

The scarab in the centre of this pectoral is inscribed with the name of 'the Lady of the House Ptahemheb, true of voice' and a spell to prevent her heart from revealing any of her sins to the gods who admitted souls to heaven (see also cat. no. 32):

O heart of my being, do not rise up as a witness (against me), do not make hostility before the Keeper of the Balance ... (Do not spoil) my name before the courtiers who dispose Mankind ... The heart rejoices at the judgement on me.

The scarab is borne upon a sacred boat and flanked by magical signs (the *djed*-pillar of stability and the *tit*-sign of protection) and the goddesses Isis and Nephthys, who protected the mummy from evil. The whole scene is framed by a rectangular shrine. This particular pectoral design was first found among the jewellery of Tutankhamun.

Like funerary jewellery, many of the ornaments worn in life were based on magical symbols and signs which were thought to have protective or beneficial powers. Such may be the explanation of the lizards, a rare motif in Egypt, which form the main element of the necklace (cat. no. 31). They are a symbol of regeneration in funerary contexts, and the drawing of a lizard looking much like these was the sign for 'many' (*asha*) in hieroglyphic writing. Its use here may have connoted rebirth and longevity (many years) or some such favourable concept.

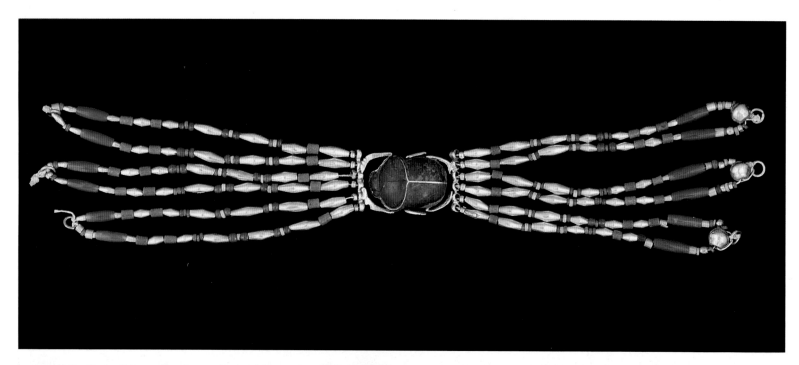

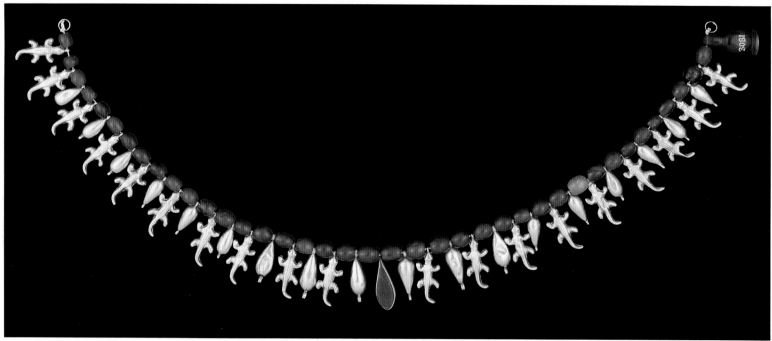

cat. no. 27   cat. no. 31

78

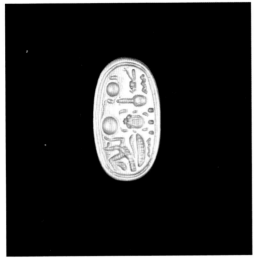

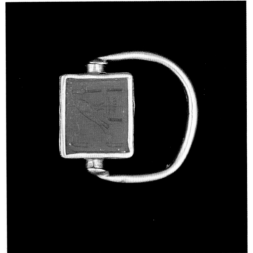

cat. no. 28   cat. no. 29   cat. no. 30

The Weighing of the Heart

Vignette from the *Book of the Dead* of Hunefer
c.1310 BC, 19th Dynasty (New Kingdom)
Egypt (Memphis?)
painted papyrus
32.0 x 87.5 cm (image)
cat. no. 32

The Egyptian Day of Judgement, on which it was decided whether to allow the deceased into the next life, was a peculiar trial of virtue known as the 'Weighing of the Heart'. The spells for surviving this inquisition became an essential inclusion in the *Book of the Dead*, an illustrated text on papyrus (Egyptian paper) with which every Egyptian who could afford it would be buried to ensure a smooth passage to the hereafter — the 'Field of Reeds' as the Egyptians called it. Because of its critical importance, this scene is also one of the most frequently illustrated in the 'vignettes' (small paintings) which are incorporated in the more elaborate and expensive copies of the text. The example shown here, from the funerary papyrus of Hunefer, the royal scribe and steward of Pharaoh Seti I, is one of the finest and best preserved of all.

The dead Hunefer is shown on the left in a diaphanous white garment being led by jackal-headed Anubis. Hunefer watches anxiously as his heart — shown as a brown pot-shaped object — is weighed on a balance against the feather of Maat, symbolic of a broad Egyptian concept embracing something like our notions of truth, righteousness and cosmic order. Anubis is shown again squatting on a podium steadying the balance's plumb-bob. This weighing was the crucial test of the dead man's virtue: a good heart would balance the feather; a bad heart, laden with sin, would not. Ammit (literally 'she who gobbles down') — a monstrous creature with the head of a crocodile, the foreparts of a lion and the hindquarters of a hippopotamus — always waits nearby, ready to devour anyone found wanting. She is shown here turning ravenously as Hunefer, having passed his ordeal, is led away. Ibis-headed Thoth, Lord of Divine Writing, records the result of the weighing before a parade of assessor gods who witness the fairness of the proceedings

and pronounce on the deceased. The texts enumerate forty-two of these assessors but they are rarely all illustrated; here fourteen of them (mostly from a group of nine important deities known as the Ennead) are shown at the top of the scene, worshipped at the left by the deceased.

The Egyptians frankly acknowledged that the souls of the dead were unlikely to be entirely faultless, but they believed that if enough declarations of innocence were made and the appropriate spells uttered one might pass the tribunal anyway. Hunefer's text (written on a later sheet of the series) is quite forthright in declaring itself as: 'What should be said when arriving at this Hall of Justice, purging Hunefer of all the evil which he has done'. He was to profess his innocence of all ill-deeds, which more complete versions of the text (Hunefer's is abbreviated at this point) enumerate at great length:

> I have done no evil, I have not deprived the orphan of his property, I have not done what the gods detest ... I have not caused (anyone) pain, I have not made (anyone) hungry ... I have not taken away the food of the spirits, I have not copulated (unlawfully) ... I have not robbed ... I have not killed men ... I am pure, pure, pure, pure!

He was also to deny some things we would hardly class as serious crimes: 'I have not been sullen ... I have not eavesdropped ... I have not babbled ... I have not been hot-tempered ... I have not been impatient'.

Perhaps the strangest spell of all was that addressed to the deceased's own heart to prevent it from giving testimony against him. This is given in the left half of the main text on this sheet, but it was also supposed to be written on a stone scarab placed over the mummy's heart (see cat. no. 29). It runs:

> O my heart, do not stand up as a witness against me, do not be opposed to me in the tribunal, do not be hostile to me in the presence of the Keeper of the Balance, for you are my *ka*-soul which was in my body ... Go forth to the happy place whereto we speed; do not make my name stink to the Entourage (of assessors) in the presence of the Great God (Osiris).

The outcome, of course, is always assumed to be favourable. In the right half of the text

here Thoth reports the verdict. In the full version (Hunefer's text is abbreviated) this reads: 'I have judged the heart of the deceased and his soul stands as a witness for him. His deeds are righteous in the great balance, and no sin has been found in him'. To this the assessor gods reply: 'This utterance of yours is true. The vindicated Osiris ... has no sin ... Ammit shall not be permitted to have power over him'.

And so the illustration shows Hunefer being introduced by falcon-headed Horus-the-Avenger-of-his-Father to Osiris, with whom all worthy deceased became mystically united. The Great God sits enthroned in an elaborate shrine wearing the *atef*-crown, backed by his sisters Isis and Nephthys and with the mummiform Sons of Horus set before him on a lotus flower. 'I bring to you Hunefer', Horus declares. 'His heart is true, having gone forth from the balance', the full version continues, '... Thoth has judged him in writing which has been told to the Ennead [i.e. the Assessors], and Maat the Great has witnessed. Let there be given to him bread and beer ... and he will be forever like the Followers of Horus'.

Like most funerary papyri at this time, Hunefer's *Book of the Dead*, measuring five and a half metres in length, was rolled up, tied and sealed with a lump of clay. This scroll would then have been placed in his tomb on or in the coffin, or inside a hollow wooden figure of the funerary deity Ptah-Sokar-Osiris. More rarely, funerary papyri were inserted among the bandages of the mummy.

cat. no. 32

The gods Sokar-Osiris, Opet and Hathor

Vignette from the *Book of the Dead* of the scribe Ani
c.1250 BC, 19th Dynasty (New Kingdom)
Egypt (Thebes?)
painted papyrus
31.5 x 53.5 cm (image)
cat. no. 33

This painting from the *Book of the Dead* of the scribe Ani shows three funerary deities receiving offerings from the deceased and his wife, who were represented in the next sheet to the left presenting heavily laden tables of food.

Osiris, Lord of the Dead, appears on the left of this sheet in the falcon-headed form which indicates his identification with Sokar, a lesser funerary god. Sometimes Ptah, too, was merged with the others to form the three-in-one deity Ptah-Sokar-Osiris. Here the ruler of the hereafter holds Osiris' standard insignia, the royal crook and flail, as well as a longer *was*-sceptre symbolizing divine power and prosperity and happiness for the deceased. He wears the distinctive Osirian *atef*-crown with ostrich plumes on either side.

According to most versions of the legend, Osiris was originally an earthly ruler (he was credited with introducing agriculture and wine-growing) who became a god of the dead through the evil scheming of his jealous brother Seth. In late accounts he is lured into a chest, cast into the Nile to drown and then dismembered by the evil Seth. The dead Osiris was recovered by his loving sister-wife Isis and embalmed by Anubis, who thereby invented mummification. The god was then brought back to life by Thoth and Horus, who fed Osiris his life-giving eye, the *wedjat* (Eye of Horus). In this way Osiris was magically resurrected and became forever Lord of the Netherworld (*duat*), the abode of the transfigured dead. Souls admitted to this world were thought to be magically united with the god himself, each one becoming 'the Osiris so-and-so'.

In the middle of the scene, the fertility goddess Opet, in the form of a hippopotamus, stands before two tables heavily laden with offerings. In her hands she bears the *ankh*-sign symbolizing life, and a linen torch to give heat and light to the deceased and destroy evil forces. She rests her left arm on the *sa*-sign of protection, for despite the fearsome combination of a hippo's head and torso, lion's legs, crocodile's tail and human breasts, Opet was a beneficent deity whose monstrous form was thought to frighten away evil forces. In this painting she wears Hathor's crown of a sun-disc between cow's horns.

Hathor herself is shown in the form of a cow on the right, stepping from behind the Western Mountain into the papyrus-fringed Nile valley. The desert edge is where tombs were built and Ani's pyramid-topped funerary chapel appears here at the foot of the mountain. As well as her standard crown — here topped by a pair of ostrich plumes — Hathor wears around her neck the *menat*-collar, a looped, beaded necklace thought to have magical powers of healing. The accompanying text praises the goddess as 'Lady of the West ... Lady of the Sacred Land; Eye of the sun-god Re which is on his forehead; kindly of countenance in the Barque of Millions of Years'.

Hathor was originally a sky-goddess (Lady of the Sky) and became the symbolic mother of the pharaoh, whom she is sometimes shown suckling. From fertility and birth her domain extended also to rebirth, and Hathor thus became the special protectress of the cemeteries of Thebes, where an image of the cow-goddess is never far from sight.

The irregularity of form and texture in landscape presented special problems for an art which tried to reduce as many features as possible to shorthand pictorial formulas and stylized symbols. The mountain which obscures Hathor's body becomes hardly recognizable in the parallel lines and bands of hatching, devoid of perspective or any other naturalistic pictorial devices, which mark its presence. Symbolism does not work well here, and it is no accident that there are no great landscapes in Egyptian art.

Ani, the owner of this funerary papyrus, was a senior temple official in Thebes. His title was 'Royal Scribe, Accounting Scribe for Divine Offerings of all the Gods, Overseer of the Granaries of the Lords of Tawer'. His beautifully illustrated *Book of the Dead* is exceptionally long and full, measuring more than twenty-three metres in length.

cat. no. **33**

Satirical painting of animals as humans

*c.*1250–1150 BC, 19th or 20th Dynasty
(New Kingdom)
Egypt (Thebes ?)
painted papyrus
9.0 x 54.5 cm

cat. no. **34**

The Egyptians' love of animals is vividly and amusingly displayed in this satirical papyrus showing animals behaving like humans. The activities are those in which the deceased are commonly represented in funerary art — playing games, herding animals and so on — and the artist was probably a member of the community of craftsmen who spent their lives decorating tombs in the Theban cemeteries. A number of mischievously satirical sketches in this vein, lightly mocking life in the hereafter, have been found among the remains of their village. Most are quick sketches on discarded potsherds or rock fragments, but this is one of a rarer class in which images were more carefully composed and painted on papyrus, clearly intended to be kept.

On the left an antelope and a lion are shown playing *senet*, an Egyptian board game much like draughts. It is the lion's move and he gives a triumphant grin. Behind him, a fox with a bag slung across his shoulder on a stick shepherds a herd of goats while his companion with a staff leads the way. In front of them a tabby cat herds a flock of geese. As if to drive home the irony, the cat carries a small gosling, too young to keep up, in its paw. On the right, a lion is engaged in sexual pursuits with a donkey lying on its back on a bed.

The painter has a good hand and a light touch which give the work a vitality and freshness rarely seen in more serious Egyptian art. Its virtues are those of the cartoon sketch over the laboured masterpiece, and like many Walt Disney creations today, its appeal stems largely from the engagingly human expressions the artist manages to give to his animal subjects: the triumphant grin of the game-playing lion, the quizzical smile of the cat, and the smug smirk of the cunning fox. Egyptian art is rarely lighthearted and this is an outstanding gem of playful art at its best.

The inversion of the natural order of things that is implied in cats tending geese, lions playing games with antelope and (on another sheet of this papyrus) cats waiting on a mouse, reappears in other satirical works. Some have seen this unlikely reversal as a satirical comment on the social turbulence which accompanied foreign incursions into Egypt, but such themes are also the stuff of folk tales — could this have illustrated an Egyptian *Aesop's Fables*? — or may simply reflect the healthy irreverence of funerary craftsmen towards what must have been considered deeply serious work.

cat. no. **34**

Ram-god and turtle-god

Statues representing demons of the underworld
*c.*1310 BC, 18th Dynasty (New Kingdom)
from the tomb of Horemheb, Valley of the Kings,
Thebes, Egypt
plaster, linen and bitumen on wood
ram 54.0 cm height; turtle 37.0 cm height
cat. no. 35

The Egyptian underworld was inhabited by a multitude of minor deities and demons who would help or hinder the deceased on their way to heaven. In interpreting this dark and mysterious world, the fertile Egyptian imagination was given free rein and the taste for unnatural hybrids predictably came to the fore, producing a plethora of monstrous creatures which freely combine human and animal forms. Most commonly a human body was given an animal's head, as in these sculptures from the tomb of King Horemheb. One has the head of a ram, the other a whole turtle.

Amun, Khnum and a few other major gods are sometimes shown with a ram's head (cat. no. 47) but the pose of this figure — seated with outstretched arms — marks it unmistakably as one of the underworld gods illustrated in the *Book of the Dead* who assist in 'repelling the enemy of Osiris [i.e. the deceased]'. In their hands these deities hold knives, snakes and lizards (both animals sometimes symbols of regeneration, but here probably representing noxious forces), and so too, no doubt, did this sculpture. Lost also are the ram's twisted horns, for which the attachment holes are visible in the top of the head.

The turtle was reviled in Egyptian religion as an evil and unclean animal. A taboo forbade eating its flesh, and scenes of the king spearing turtles in the Nile symbolize the triumph of good over evil rather than genuine sport. The animal's shadowy, secretive existence led to its being regarded as a particular enemy of the sun-god Re. 'Re lives, the turtle is dead!' a spell in the *Book of the Dead* repeats a number of times.

The figure shown here bearing a turtle on his shoulders in the guise of a head, was one of the 'Gatekeepers of the Sixth Division (of the underworld), who keep watch for Osiris'. In order to reach heaven, the dead had to pass through a number of these gates, each guarded by a triad of monstrous beings. Only those who could recount the demons' names would be let through. The turtle-headed gatekeeper was known as the 'Eater of Filth', an allusion to the turtle's supposedly unclean habits. He is shown in exactly the pose of this sculpture on later royal coffins, holding a knife in his lower hand; this piece was no doubt armed in the same way when it was first made.

These two sculptures were among the few objects left behind by robbers in the tomb of Horemheb, a man of humble origins who rose to prominence as a general under Akhenaten, and finally succeeded to the throne itself (after the short reigns of Ai and Tutankhamun) as the last pharaoh of the Eighteenth Dynasty (1319–1307 BC). Sculptures of underworld deities seem to have been a royal prerogative, and what is probably a reference to another such set is preserved on an ostracon (potsherd inscription) which mentions 'the gods' being taken into the tomb of the Nineteenth-Dynasty pharaoh Merneptah.

Both sculptures are carved from wood which has been covered with plaster and linen, and then liberally painted with bitumen.

cat. no. **35**

Coffin of Henutmehyt, chantress of Amun

c.1300–1200 BC, 19th Dynasty (New Kingdom)
Thebes, Egypt
gilded and painted plaster on wood
2.08 m height

cat. no. 36

Of the hundreds of priestly burials found at Thebes, few are as elaborate and lavishly decorated as the gold-covered coffins of the chantress Henutmehyt. Inside the anthropoid ('human-form') coffin shown here there was also an inner coffin and a mummy cover (cat. no. 37), both fully gilded. Nothing is known of Henutmehyt, but judging by her splendid burial she was a priestess of some means.

Coffins of this period are more richly decorated than before, though the designs are not yet cramped and chaotic, as they were to become in the Twenty-first Dynasty (cat. nos 38, 39). Henutmehyt's coffin strikes a good balance — lavish but not yet overblown.

Gold leaf is used to great dramatic effect by setting it against the pitch-black mass of the elaborately plaited hair and obsidian eyes. Being a woman, Henutmehyt is shown with the hands outstretched (men usually have them clenched) and bears on her head the standard sheaf of lotus blossoms, whose reappearance from the water each day made them a symbol of rebirth. It was customary to show both sexes lavishly bejewelled. In this period the jewellery was modelled in low relief plaster and then painted or gilded. Below a massive beaded necklace Henutmehyt wears a rectangular pectoral in which she is shown adoring Re's solar barque (the ship in which the sun-god travelled through the underworld) flanked by Eyes of Horus. At the bottom of the gilded section, the kneeling figure of the sky-goddess Nut spreads her wings protectively.

The painted yellow background of the lower half of the coffin continues the gold-like effect without the expense. The figures are painted in blue, red and black, the colours now somewhat yellowed by an overcoat of varnish. Strips of text echo the positions of the mummy's final bandaging. An address to Nut in the column of hieroglyphs below the sky-goddess describes Henutmehyt as a 'Lady of the House, chantress of Amun'. On either side are figures of the four Sons of Horus who protected the embalmed organs: human-headed Imsety, baboon-headed Hapy, jackal-headed Duamutef and falcon-headed Qebehsenuef. At the feet of the coffin are upside-down figures of Isis and Nephthys, the sisters of Osiris who gathered up and preserved his dismembered body. The sides of the coffin show the Sons of Horus again, along with Anubis and Thoth, and short inscriptions in which these deities promise to protect the deceased, as they had Osiris.

But even their strong magic was not always enough. Wallis Budge, who acquired Henutmehyt's coffin for the British Museum soon after its discovery in 1887, records how the mummy inside the inner coffin was found wrapped from head to foot in large sheets of papyrus inscribed with the *Book of the Dead*. 'When these were removed', he reported, 'the mummy was an oblong black shapeless mass, which was stuck to the bottom of the coffin, and to get it out it had to be broken in pieces'.

Henutmehyt lived in the Nineteenth Dynasty (1295–1187 BC), the period which produced the last great warrior pharaohs of the New Kingdom. Its founders had made their capital at Thebes, and Amun, the chief god of the city, now fused with the sun-god as Amun-Re, rose to a position of unparalleled pre-eminence. His chief temple at Karnak was made ever grander, surpassing anything built in Egypt before, and the priesthood came to wield unrivalled powers.

Women rarely played a major role in Egyptian cults, usually functioning only as singers, musicians and ceremonial actors. At Thebes, however, things were different. During the New Kingdom and later, priestesses came to play an increasingly prominent role in Amun's cortège. A number of high offices were reserved exclusively for women, including a 'God's Spouse', who was regarded as Amun's terrestrial wife.

cat. no. **36**

Mummy cover of Henutmehyt, chantress of Amun

c.1300–1200 BC, 19th Dynasty (New Kingdom)
Thebes, Egypt
gilded and painted cartonnage; inlaid eyes of
crystalline limestone and obsidian
69.0 cm height
cat. no. 37

During the New Kingdom (1550–1070 BC) Egyptian burials became increasingly elaborate as more and more care and expense was devoted to the proper disposal of the dead. Instead of just one coffin, those who could afford it would now have a sequence of up to four. The outer coffin might be rectangular; the others were always mummy-shaped, made in decreasing sizes to be set one inside the other like a Russian doll. Inside the coffins, directly over the mummy itself, would be placed a mummy cover, whose decoration repeated the main designs of the lid of the innermost coffin. Early covers of the Eighteenth and Nineteenth Dynasties, like this example, were often made in two pieces which met at the waist.

This is the upper part of the mummy cover of the chantress Henutmehyt, whose outer coffin is also displayed here (cat. no. 36). The singer's mummy, found under the cover, was wrapped in large sheets of papyrus bearing extracts from the *Book of the Dead*.

Like the coffins, the mummy cover of Henutmehyt is gilded except for the painted black hair and obsidian eyes, which provide a dramatic contrast with the glittering gold. She lies with her arms crossed on her chest, the position that had been standard in representations of the dead for a century or so. The low-relief decoration shows the nipples of her partly exposed breasts patterned like flowers, the multiple strings of her beaded collar, and the folds of a fine garment pushed back at the elbows. At the bottom, a rectangular pectoral bears the sacred boat of the sun-god Re.

Since the cover fitted directly over the mummy, the proportions of the face and shoulders are less enlarged than on the coffins, each of which had to be larger than the one inside. Her face is serene and contented, the state in which she and every other Egyptian hoped they would spend eternity after a trouble-free passage to the 'Field of Reeds'.

The cover is made of cartonnage, consisting of layers of linen stiffened with plaster. In this case the cartonnage was painted red before the gold leaf was applied, giving it a noticeably reddish tinge.

The lower part of Henutmehyt's mummy cover, placed over her lower torso and legs, is an open framework design which was gilded all over before being backed with purple linen. This linen still survives but is too fragile to be transported. The strips of the openwork design correspond to the positions of the final bandages wrapped around the mummy.

cat. no. 37

Coffin and mummy of a chantress of Amun

c.970 BC, late 21st Dynasty (3rd Intermediate Period)
Egypt (Thebes?)
painted plaster on wood coffin; embalmed body wrapped in linen
coffin 1.88 m height
cat. no. 38

Nothing looms larger in the popular conception of ancient Egypt than the mummy. This macabre burial practice derives from the belief that the dead person's survival in the after-life depended on the preservation of his or her physical body, in which the deceased's *ka*-spirit — the embodiment of the vital life-force or genius — would continue to reside and, in some magical way, to eat, breathe, and see just as it had in life. For this reason, the Egyptians contemplated with horror the decay or improper treatment of their physical remains, and went to great lengths to ensure that the appropriate rites were observed. Wretched indeed was the barbaric Asiatic (as the Egyptians regarded all Easterners) who was simply 'placed in a sheepskin' and buried in the ground. 'It is no small matter', a king reminded an exiled official to lure him home, 'that thy corpse be properly buried!'.

The Egyptians began experimenting with treatments to preserve bodies around the time of the great pyramids (about 2600 BC) and continued to improve the technique over many centuries. By the New Kingdom a basic method had been developed, with variations according to wealth and status. The mummies of the Twenty-first Dynasty, like the one shown here, are generally the most careful and sophisticated. Later embalmers often took short-cuts which today, after twenty-five centuries, leave little more than a blackened shrivelled mass. It is from this that the word 'mummy' derives, *mummiya* being the Arabic for 'bitumen'; later Egyptians used the word to describe the darkened corpses of badly embalmed bodies in the mistaken belief that they had been dipped in tar.

The embalming process used for fine burials like this was long and complicated, accompanied at every stage by rigidly prescribed spells and prayers. First the corpse was washed and the face covered with molten resin to keep it supple. An instrument was then inserted through the nose to chop up the brain and remove the pieces, which were discarded. The brain cavity was refilled with sawdust or resin-soaked linen. A ceremonial obsidian knife was then used to make an incision in the left side of the abdomen, from which the stomach and intestines were removed; next, puncturing the diaphragm, the lungs and liver were extracted. The heart, believed to be the seat of intelligence, was carefully left intact. The body was then rinsed with palm wine and spices and buried for forty days in natron, a naturally occurring salt. This effected the essential dehydration of the body, reducing its weight by seventy-five per cent and leaving the corpse a dark brown colour. The body was then washed and dried and the stomach restuffed. In earlier periods sawdust, natron or resin-soaked linen were used to fill the cavity, and the extracted organs — which had meanwhile also been dehydrated, embalmed with resins and wrapped in linen — were placed in special 'canopic' jars. But in the Twenty-first Dynasty these mummified organs were put back inside the body together with figurines of the four Sons of Horus, each of whom was responsible for preserving one of the four organs. Any excess space was filled with sawdust. The shrivelled skin was restored by rubbing in a sweet-smelling lotion of juniper oil, beeswax, natron, spices, milk and wine. The incision was then sealed with molten resin and covered with a plate of gold or wax bearing an Eye of Horus, symbol of the powerful magic which had restored life to Osiris and would prevent evil from entering the corpse.

At this stage the rest of the body was still very shrunken. To remedy this, the embalmers of the Twenty-first Dynasty would make new incisions and insert linen or a mud-sawdust mixture under the skin of the face and limbs, filling out the flesh that the dehydration process had dissolved. The nostrils, ears and mouth were plugged with linen or wax, and the eyes pushed down into their sockets, covered with linen and the eyelids pulled over. The whole corpse was then coated with molten resin to make it tough and waterproof. As a final touch, the skin might be coloured (red for men, yellow for women) and a woman's face made up.

Then the bandaging began. This took fifteen days and could use 400 square metres of linen, in up to twenty layers of shrouds and bandages which were frequently coated with resin. Imitation jewellery and magical amulets were placed between the layers to ward off evil. A pair of crossed leather straps — looking much like modern braces — would sometimes be placed on the chest and painted, as here, on the inner coffin. They were often stamped with the name of the reigning pharaoh and high-priest of Amun, but otherwise their purpose is unknown. The whole embalming process took some seventy days.

An X-ray of the mummy shows it to be a woman — no doubt a chantress of Amun — aged between thirty-five and forty-eight, lying with her hands over the pubic area. The coffin in which she was found, however, was originally made for a man — as the clenched fists, painted beard-straps and bearded illustrations of the *ba*-bird prove. Such reuse of coffins, even for mummies of different sexes, was quite common in the Twenty-first Dynasty. The painted decoration shows the standard array of funerary gods and magic symbols, including winged images of the sun-disc Re, Nut (kneeling) and hawk-headed Re-Harakhti, as well as scarab beetles of the rising sun Khepri, flanked by enthroned deities.

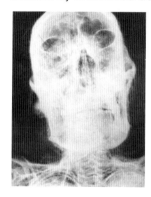

X-ray of mummy. (British Museum)

cat. no. 38

93

Mummy cover of a chantress of Amun-Re

c.970 BC, late 21st Dynasty (3rd Intermediate
Period)
Egypt (Thebes?)
painted plaster on wood
1.62 m height
cat. no. 39

Ironically, it is the ancient tomb robbers that
we have to thank for the survival of so many
mummies and coffins of Twenty-first Dynasty
priests and priestesses. During the twelfth
and eleventh centuries BC, tomb looting
had reached such proportions that, around
970 BC, the priests of Thebes secretly
assembled all the mummies they could
salvage from the Valley of the Kings and the
individual priests' burials, and reinterred
them in a few large, well-hidden tombs. The
discovery of two of these big hoards in the
late nineteenth century brought to light the
largest groups of royal and priestly burials
ever found. The so-called 'royal cache' was
discovered, probably in 1871, by local
villagers who disturbed the tomb and sold
much of its contents before the authorities
were alerted. But the 'second cache', containing some 153 coffins of Twenty-first
Dynasty priests and priestesses, including
101 double sets, was found intact in 1891.
This cover, whose exact findspot is unknown,
probably came from one of the many smaller
stashes found by the locals in the eighteenth
and nineteenth centuries.

After being embalmed, mummies were
placed inside elaborately decorated coffins
(cat. nos 36, 38, 40), the innermost layer of
which consisted of a decorated cover placed
directly over the mummy itself. In the Twenty-
first Dynasty these covers were made in a
single piece which ran the full length of the
mummy. A web of folklore now surrounds
this cover, which somehow acquired a
reputation for bringing bad luck. Its most
notorious 'curse' (such ideas did not start
with Tutankhamun!) was said to have been
the sinking of the Titanic. The story somehow
got about that this mummy cover was on that
doomed ship when it struck an iceberg on
its maiden cruise to America. Such was the
strength of these baseless rumours that the
Keeper of Egyptian Antiquities at the British

Museum later felt obliged to put the record
straight: 'No mummy which did things of this
kind was ever in the British Museum', he
wrote. 'The cover never went on the Titanic
. . . It never went to America'.

The colour scheme of the coffins — red
and blue (often faded to green) on a yellow
background — imitated the splendid royal
coffins, like that of Tutankhamun, made of
gold inlaid with colourful stones. They follow
closely the form of the mummified body
which lay underneath, except that the arms
are crossed on the chest rather than by the
sides. Men's hands are shown clenched,
often holding amulets, while those of women
usually extend outwards. The impossibly
horizontal disposition of this cover's hands,
as if no arms existed, is a peculiarity of the
late Twenty-first Dynasty. The fingernails are
coloured to show the staining of henna.
Both sexes wear the striped wig, which on
women may be plaited or decorated.

The decoration of coffins and covers
reached an unprecedented degree of
elaboration in the Twenty-first Dynasty. The
painting becomes smaller and more cramped
as designs spread all over the surfaces,
filling every available space with figures,
magic symbols and sacred writings. The
result is not only an illustrated guide to the
mythology and funerary beliefs of the period,
but also some very fine painting.

The elaborate scenes on this cover show
the usual array of gods, demons and magical
symbols. Below a beaded collar the sun-
disc spreads its wings over the morning sun,
pushed upwards by the scarab beetle Khepri
and adored by baboons and animal-headed
gods. Osiris, the god of the dead, is shown
below the kneeling figure of the winged sky-
god Nut as a djed-pillar, holding twin sets of
the royal crook and flail, and again, in the
next register down, seated in human form
and flanked by the animal-headed Sons
of Horus holding snakes. Just above the
winged sun-disc, at the very bottom of the
cover, the name of Amenophis I is written in
an oval cartouche. Amenophis I, second
king of the Eighteenth Dynasty, reorganized
the priesthood of Amun-Re, King of the
Gods, and endowed the large temple estates

at Thebes, for which he was revered ever
after by Amun's devotees. The other texts
among the figures are standard prayers for
funerary offerings.

The cover is made of wood, which was
coated with a thin layer of plaster before
being painted. The hands were made
separately and attached with dowels. A final
coat of varnish is responsible for the over-all
yellowish tinge which now obscures the
original colours.

cat. no. 39

Inner coffin base of Amenemopet, priest of Amun-Re

c.920 BC, early 22nd Dynasty (3rd Intermediate Period)
Thebes, Egypt
painted wood
2.10 m height
cat. no. 40

The coffins of the Twenty-first and early Twenty-second Dynasties were more elaborately decorated than ever before. The interiors of the coffins, previously left blank, were now covered with religious scenes and texts relating to the underworld gods, the embalming of the deceased and his passage into the next world. In the New Kingdom such scenes, mainly from the *Book of What Is in the Underworld*, had been depicted on the walls of the tombs. But in the following centuries, when most people were buried in reused tombs or caches, the scenes were transferred to the coffins, which therefore had to convey all the magic necessary to ensure the soul's passage into the other world.

Because they were not varnished, the colours of the interiors are not yellowed and faded like the outer surfaces, and so retain their full polychrome brilliance. The artist of this piece — the base of the inner coffin of a priest — had a steady hand and a good sense of design, and he rendered his subjects with painstaking attention to detail. Such work bears comparison with the best of any period. But it is not creative art in anything like the modern or even the ancient Greek sense. Painters worked to established guidelines which dictated how everything should be rendered, down to the finest detail. As with much ancient art, the virtues of their work are therefore those of fine craftsmanship — care, technical skill, and fidelity to conventional forms.

As on the coffin's exterior, the inside surface is crammed with deities and magic symbols. At the head of the coffin, in an oval cartouche, appears the name of the deified pharaoh Amenophis I, whose cult tended to replace aspects of Osiris worship in the New Kingdom. His cartouche is flanked by figures of the sister goddesses Isis and Nephthys. The next register down shows the dead man, wearing a priestly panther skin, making offerings — shown piled on tables — to falcon-headed Re-Harakhti and jackal-headed Anubis, all identified by their names and titles in the accompanying texts. Further down, the dead man's *ba* — an aspect of his spirit shown as a human-headed bird — worships enthroned figures of Osiris, who is described in the oval cartouche as 'Lord of Abydos, perfect of being'. In the next scene we see the embalming-god Anubis purifying the mummy by pouring over it a libation. Everywhere the spaces are filled with magic amuletic symbols — the winged sun-disc, the Eye of Horus (*wedjat*), the life-sign (*ankh*), and along the bottom the *djed*-pillar of stability and the *tit*-sign of protection. On the sides of the interior are rows of nightmarish mummiform deities of the underworld with animals' heads.

The outside of the coffin bears elaborate scenes showing the funeral ceremony and the sun-god's journey through the underworld. In the main scene on the right side we see the mummy drawn in procession on its funerary barque (a ship-shaped shrine) lamented by wailing women. In an unusual deviation from the profile rule, one of the women's faces is shown frontally and a child is seen in three-quarter view. To the right, a priest with a pot of unguent and a special instrument performs the Opening of the Mouth on the upright mummy at the cemetery, while another priest reads spells from a papyrus, and a third, dressed in a panther skin, pours a libation and burns incense. This crucial ceremony restored the mummy's senses so that it could function once again in its posthumous existence. A woman pours a libation over a liberally stacked table of offerings, watched by the man's soul in the form of the human-headed *ba*-bird.

The left side of the coffin is decorated with scenes showing the sacred boat of the sun-god Re being towed through the underworld at night, accompanied by other deities: Isis and Nephthys at the front, the scarab Khepri at the rear. It was this same treacherous course that the dead had to negotiate to reach the after-life. The cortège approaches an offering table, greeted by a sphinx and two funerary deities associated with mummification: Nephthys and Anubis. To the left, a man pours a libation over a large vase of flowers and a woman raises her hands in greeting to the goddess Hathor, who is shown as a cow appearing from behind the Western Mountain near a tomb (see cat. no. 33). Souls of the deceased adore the goddess, one touching her udder, another drinking from the libation.

Amenemopet calls himself 'divine father of Amun, king of the gods, overseer of the mysteries of the Temple of Amun'. He came from a long line of Amun priests, his father and grandfather having held similar offices. This was a common occurrence in the Twenty-first Dynasty, which saw the establishment of many clerical 'dynasties'; as the priesthood became more powerful it was inevitable that privileged offices should tend to pass from father to son.

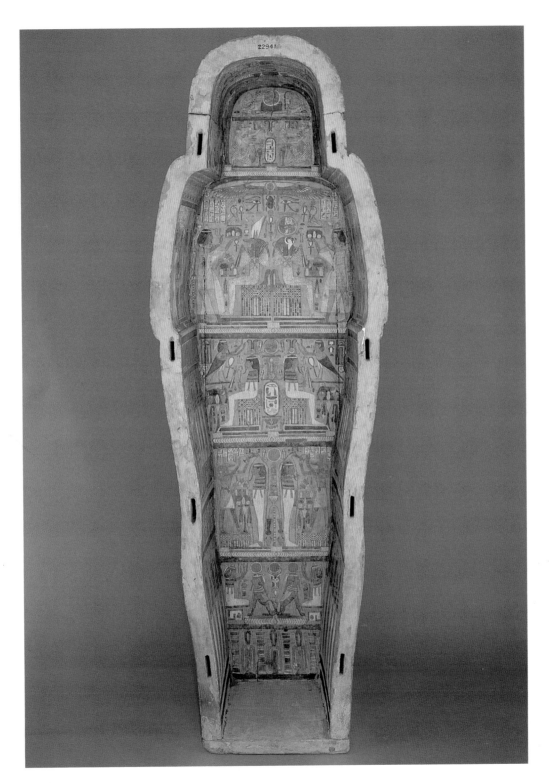

cat. no. 40

Deniuenkhons, chantress of Amun-Re

Funerary stela
c.800 BC (3rd Intermediate Period)
Egypt (Thebes?)
painted plaster on sycamore wood
33.0 cm height
cat. no. 41

Throughout Egyptian history, stone blocks (stelae) carved or painted with funerary scenes were a regular feature of all well-to-do burials. Larger tombs would have had a number of stelae, sometimes carved directly into the wall, through one of which (the false door) the *ka*-soul of the deceased could come out to receive offerings of food. The example shown here belongs to the round-topped type which became standard from Middle Kingdom times. During the New Kingdom, they were often set in niches in the brick pyramids that surmounted the funerary chapel (see cat. no. 33), but by the time of this stela, from the burial of a chantress of Amun-Re, they were simply placed in the burial chamber next to the coffin.

The dead woman is shown raising her arms in adoration before the composite solar deity Re-Harakhti-Atum, for whom she has piled high a table of offerings. Overhead, the scarab-beetle Khepri, manifesting the sun at dawn, is flanked by jackals of the embalming god Anubis. At the top, the sun-disc of 'Horus the Behdetite' — almost obligatory on curved-top stelae — spreads its wings benevolently over the scene.

The inscription is in the manner of a label, identifying the two figures. The god is described as 'Lord of the Two Lands' and the woman as a 'chantress of Amun-Re' and wife of Ankhkhons, 'head of the procession (of Sokar)'.

The elements of the scene and the way they are arranged follow standard Egyptian formulas. Indeed, the whole composition is a familiar cliché of funerary art which offers the artist little scope for originality. Nonetheless, the careful painting and fresh colours (exceptionally well preserved even by Egyptian standards) make this stela one of the very finest and most attractive of its kind.

The artist had a sure hand and has paid close attention to detail. We can make out most of the foods on the offering table: a bunch of lotus flowers, a duck, a basket of dates, two varieties of bread and (below the table) a jar of water or oil, and two ceremonial lettuces. The dead woman wears a diaphanous dress, rendered with broad bands of thinned paint which allow her body to show through. The god she worships brings together aspects of Re, the great sun-god, Harakhti, whose name means 'Horus of the Horizon', and Atum, the primeval creator who protects the dead on their journey through the underworld. From Re he gets the crown of sun-disc and cobra, from Horus (Harakhti) the falcon's head. As usual, Re-Harakhti-Atum holds the life-sign (*ankh*) in one hand and the staff of power (*was*) in the other, but the royal crook and flail are a less common addition, reflecting the god's identification with the pharaoh. The sun was intimately associated in Egyptian thought with rebirth and rejuvenation, and it is for this reason that solar deities play such a large role in funerary art. Re-Harakhti, as the newly born sun of the eastern horizon, had a special relevance for the deceased: to be united with Osiris in the other world, the dead person had to come back to life, imitating the sun's daily rebirth.

As in almost all Egyptian art, the mood — if it can be called that — is one of serene detachment. In any modern sense there is no mood at all; with all action reduced to static formulas and no attempt to portray expression or character, everything happens in the same emotional vacuum. Egyptian art had always to be 'readable' as a story or image, and its decorative conventions ensured that every act was performed with elegance and grace; but beyond this pervasive air of refinement and otherworldliness, there is nothing which comes close to conveying the real atmosphere or mood of an occasion. These ephemeral qualities were of no importance to the Egyptians, who were concerned rather with what they regarded as an eternal reality of being. Despite their belief that pictures were in a sense alive and had powers normally associated only with animate beings, their art therefore generally made little attempt to capture the psychological dimension that distinguishes the animate world.

The stela was prepared in the same way as contemporary coffins — by painting a thin coat of plaster over a wooden base. The colours here have survived very well. Blue, now turned olive-green at the surface, was applied very thickly to give the effect of low-relief carving.

Iti, priest of Amun

Block statue
702 BC, 25th Dynasty (Late Period)
Egypt, findspot unknown
painted limestone
44.5 cm height (figure only)
cat. no. 42

So-called block statues were invented by the Egyptians in the Middle Kingdom, and soon became one of the most popular types of votive offering to temples, where they served as permanent symbols of the dedicator's devotion to the god. They take their name from the block-like form in which the person is shown: sitting on the ground, legs drawn up to the chest, arms crossed over the knees, the whole body covered by an enveloping robe. This position creates a rectangular block from which only the protruding head, hands (here holding a lotus bud) and sometimes the feet needed to be carved in detail. In this statue of the priest Iti, the robe clings to the body more closely than usual, and tapers towards the feet, giving a good impression of the limbs underneath. Most other such statues treat the block in a more cursory, geometric manner.

The reason for this peculiar posture was not so much the Egyptians' tendency to reduce things to symbols as simple economy: a block is far the easiest way to represent the human form. It could be carved more quickly and cheaply, and with less risk of breakage, than any other full-figure type, and it created many conveniently flat surfaces for inscriptions. Kings were never shown in this form, but priests and wealthy private citizens would commission the best sculptors for such works, and some very fine block portraits were produced. Such is this statue of Iti, 'overseer of the harem, head of the second and third priestly guilds of the estate of Khons the Child', created at Thebes in the reign of the Twenty-fifth Dynasty pharaoh Shabaka. The inscription dates it very precisely to the eleventh day of the month Payni (the earliest known occurrence of this dating system) in the pharaoh's fifteenth regnal year (702 BC).

The crisp, sharp carving of Iti's face and wig reflect the revival of fine craftsmanship which took place under the Nubian rulers of the Twenty-fifth Dynasty. The style, too, is a return to the heyday of New Kingdom sculpture: Iti's face is the age-old conventional mask, totally untouched by the search for character and individual likeness which some sculptors were bringing to their work (compare cat. no. 43). The double wig — a smooth one over a layered one — was a New Kingdom fashion which had become rare by this time. The outer wig retains its original paint, now lost from the rest of the statue.

Inscribed on the front of the statue is a prayer in which Iti appeals to the deities Re-Harakhti, Atum and Osiris for food offerings to be made to his spirit. Then follows Iti's family tree. In Egypt most trades and professions tended to be passed on from father to son, and Iti's genealogy shows that he came from a long line of priests, his ancestors for the last five generations having also held posts in the priesthood at Thebes.

The statue would have been set into a pedestal covering the roughly-cut base.

cat. no. **42**

Portrait head of a man

From a temple statue
*c.*700–650 BC, 25th Dynasty or later
(Late Period)
Memphis, Egypt
crystalline limestone
22.7 cm height

cat. no. 43

Puffy-eyed, small-mouthed and clearly showing his age, this face could hardly be less like the idealized picture of eternal youth that is the paradigm of Egyptian art (compare cat. nos 24, 42). And yet the distinctive wig quickly assures us that it is Egyptian, and this is in fact borne out by the face itself. For despite the Egyptians' tenacious adherence to established stylistic formulas, there were periods when artists tried to capture something of their subject's physical likeness and personality. Some tentative 'character studies' of wealthy officials in the Old Kingdom provide the background to a remarkable series of pharaonic portraits in the late Middle Kingdom. Royal sculpture, which had previously resisted any indication of ageing or even humanity, shows for a brief period pharaohs with old, care-worn eyes and sunken cheeks; instead of a living god there emerges the severe, world-wise monarch, the heavy responsibility of leadership clearly visible in his austerely graven image.

Thereafter, apart from occasional throwbacks to the earlier style, and the short-lived 'Amarna revolution', when the deformed Akhenaten encouraged artists to emphasize his physical peculiarities, Egyptian sculpture reverted to its idealizing formulas for over a thousand years. Surprisingly, it was under a foreign Nubian dynasty (the Twenty-fifth) that sculptors returned again to individual facial likeness, both in royal and private statues. It is in this period, about the seventh century BC, that this head probably belongs.

The artists of the Twenty-fifth Dynasty were very aware of their forebears' achievements, and our sculptor may well have been consciously emulating the royal character studies of the Middle Kingdom. The heavy, arched upper eyelids and large ears, forced outwards by the broad wig, are features of that genre. Much to the frustration of modern scholars, Egyptian artists of this so-called Late Period copied freely from the works of earlier times as far back as the Old Kingdom.

Works such as this come as close to true portraits as any ancient artist had yet created. The Greeks produced nothing comparable for another 200 years, and when they did, it may have been partly due to the influence of works such as this. The increasingly naturalistic likenesses which were produced in Egypt from the Nubian Dynasty into the Persian Period (Twenty-seventh Dynasty), may well have played some role in broadening Greek artists' obsession with the human body to include also the character and expression that a more plausible face could bring — something their own development was leading them towards anyway. Unfortunately, the dating of most Late-Period Egyptian works is very uncertain; so much so, indeed, that a previous generation of scholars assumed any influence in Persian times to have been in the other direction — from the Classical world to Egypt — as it was in the Hellenistic and Roman periods. With only style to judge by, such matters are very difficult to decide; the intriguing possibility remains, however, that the genesis of Greek portraiture — one of the quantum leaps in ancient art — was indebted to the culture which was in so many other ways the most formal and unchanging of all — the Egyptian.

The head comes from a nearly life-size statue which would have shown the full figure, either standing, sitting or squatting in a block (see cat. no. 42). The Egyptians excelled at carving hard stone like this, for which they largely eschewed metal implements in favour of the traditional stone pounders and rubbers.

The subject would have been a man of some means, perhaps a government official, but he cannot now be identified. The statue, found at the Old Kingdom capital Memphis, would have stood in a temple as a symbol of his devotion to a god. Like most Egyptian statuary, it was probably painted.

cat. no. **43**

Shabti figurines

Shabti of Neferibresaneith
c.600–400 BC, 26th or 27th Dynasty
(Late Period)
Saqqara, Egypt
green glazed composition ('faience')
19.0 cm height

cat. no. **44**

Shabti of Hatsheret, chantress of Aten-Re
c.1375 BC, 18th Dynasty (New Kingdom)
Abydos, Egypt
ebony with white pigment
23.0 cm height

cat. no. **45**

Shabti of Psametik, 'Divine Father' and Overseer
of the Memphis Cemetery
c.600–400 BC, 26th or 27th Dynasty (Late Period)
Saqqara, Egypt
blue glazed composition ('faience')
18.5 cm height

cat. no. **46**

The Egyptians believed in an after-life much like their earthly existence. And as in life, there would be much work to be done: fields to be ploughed, crops to be harvested, grain to be stored and so on. Even noblemen would have to pull their weight, and since their mortal servants and labourers would not be available, the Egyptians resorted to magical substitutes called, at various times, *shabtis, shawabtis* or *ushabtis*.

The Egyptian word *ushabti* (as they were called in the New Kingdom) means 'answerer', and that is what these figurines would do, offering themselves for agricultural work when their master's name was called. They bear a standard inscription which is described in the *Book of the Dead* as the 'spell for causing a *shabti* to do work for a man in the realm of the dead'. The inscription on the *Shabti* of Neferibresaneith declares:

> O these shabtis, if the Osiris, the God's Father Psametik, born of Sebarekhyt, is summoned to do any of the work which is required there in the god's land . . . 'Here I am', you shall say . . . if he is summoned to make arable a field, to irrigate the riverside lands, to transport by boat the sand of the West to the East and vice versa, 'Here I am', you shall say.

Those who could afford it would have 401 *shabtis* in their tomb, 365 labourers and 36 overseers; kings had even more. The labourers, one for each day of the year, are shown mummiform, equipped for their tasks with a pick and hoe in each hand and a seed bag slung over their shoulder; some also have water pots. Sometimes supplies of miniature tools were provided for when the originals wore out. The overseer *shabtis* wore normal clothes and carried a whip to ensure that the job got done. All the *shabtis* were placed in the burial chamber in specially made boxes.

The finest *shabtis* were made in the New Kingdom (cat. no. 45) and during the revival of fine craftsmanship in the Twenty-fifth and Twenty-sixth Dynasties (cat. nos 44, 46). The earliest mummiform figurines seem to have been conceived as images of the deceased themselves, and the legacy of this origin is apparent in the New Kingdom *shabti* of the chantress Hatsheret (cat. no. 45), portrayed beardless and without any tools. The two later examples are of the usual worker type, bearing picks and hoes.

From the New Kingdom on, most *shabtis* were made from 'Egyptian faience', an artificial glazed material which was formed in moulds and then baked in a kiln. Mass-produced 'faience' *shabtis*, bearing only the most basic form of the spell inscription, have been recovered in their thousands from tombs all over Egypt; but much finer figurines like cat. nos 44 and 46, made specifically for their owners with complete versions of the spell, continued the high standards of earlier times.

Shabtis are just one aspect of a peculiar and pervasive strain in Egyptian religious thought: the belief that models and other images (such as tomb reliefs and paintings) would magically provide the same sustenance and services in death as the real people and objects had provided in life. Some Old Kingdom tombs contained sculptured 'reserve heads' of stone in case the mummy's head should be damaged or decay. In the Middle Kingdom, tombs were often supplied with small model sculptures of servants performing their daily tasks — ploughing, making bread and so on. The dead person's survival in the other world was thought to depend on the preservation of his mummified body, which, as in life, required food. This was supposed to be supplied by his family and retainers who would make offerings of food in his tomb chapel. But should these fail — the Egyptians were a pragmatic people — the models and tomb reliefs, which showed the same activities, were believed to act as a back-up. Just by representing food production and writing spells declaring that it would sustain the deceased, the Egyptians imagined that these things would magically happen.

cat. no. **44**

cat. no. **45**

cat. no. **46**

Statuettes of deities

Khnum
after 600 BC (Late Period)
Egypt, findspot unknown
bronze with gold and silver inlay
23.0 cm height
cat. no. 47

Soul (ba) of Pe
after 600 BC (Late Period)
Egypt, findspot unknown
bronze
20.5 cm height
cat. no. 48

Sphinx
after 600 BC (Late Period)
Egypt, findspot unknown
bronze
17.0 cm height
cat. no. 49

The unique fascination of ancient Egypt to peoples of other cultures up to the present day stems in no small part from the bizarre menagerie of weird and wonderful creatures with which one is confronted at almost every turn in Egyptian art: on the walls of temples and tombs, in statuary, and even on personal trinkets and jewellery. In direct contrast to the Greeks, who conceived their gods in the image of man, the Egyptians pictured many of their deities wholly or partly in the forms of animals: sometimes a natural animal or a fanciful combination of animal parts, but mostly monstrous hybrids with the head of an animal and the body of a man or woman. This, more than anything, is responsible for the aura of occult mystery which has surrounded Egyptian culture in the West ever since its discovery by the Greeks.

The creator-god Khnum is shown here with the head of his sacred animal the ram (cat. no. 47). Striding forward in the age-old manner (see cat. no. 21), he originally held a staff in the left hand and an amuletic symbol in the right (both now lost). He wears the *atef*-crown with its distinctive ostrich plumes at the sides and a gilded sun-disc at the base. The twisted horns on the crown were also originally gilded, and the toenails on the statue were covered with silver.

Khnum was 'the father of fathers, the mother of mothers' who fashioned men and gods in clay on a potter's wheel and implanted them as seeds in their mothers' bodies. As the universal creator he sometimes appears with four heads, bringing together Re (the sun and heaven), Shu (the air), Osiris (the netherworld) and Geb (the earth), and is the guardian of the source of the Nile, the lifeblood of the country.

The larger falcon-headed figure (cat. no. 48) represents one of the Souls of Pe. According to later tradition, the town of Pe was the capital of northern Egypt in the Predynastic Period, and these 'city-souls' of the north are matched by a parallel series of jackal-headed Souls of Nekhen, the Predynastic capital of the south. Both seem originally to have been regarded as personifications of the deified Predynastic rulers of their respective capitals, but later these city-souls assumed the more general role of genii of Upper and Lower Egypt, whose association with the king in art symbolized the protection and support given to him by the Two Lands. The Souls of Pe are generally shown, as in this figure, kneeling on one leg, beating their chests with one hand and raising the other in a fist. This peculiarly Egyptian expression of reverence and jubilation seems to have been how the Souls of Pe would greet the rising sun, or welcome the dead king into the next world. Funerary texts describe them dancing, clapping their hands and beating their chests in celebration of the pharaoh's resurrection. 'O Osiris the king', they exclaim, 'you have died, but you shall live!'.

This figure is a very fine work, larger than usual, and surprisingly animated. The loss of inlay work in the cheeks, eyes and wig leaves the face rather mask-like; we have to imagine it gleaming with precious metal or coloured stone. The statuette is clothed in a close-fitting kilt, hardly distinguishable from the body, to which it clings like a membrane. The body itself is powerfully modelled with an unusually emphatic treatment of the muscles, especially the legs, though much is still streamlined for elegance. The rough-filed effect of the surface, lending the work a fresh, almost modern, quality, is probably the result of over-zealous nineteenth-century cleaning; the original finish would have been smooth.

Human heads on animal bodies are more rare than the reverse. The only common Egyptian beings of this type were the *ba*-soul (conceived as a human-headed bird) and the sphinx — a lion with a man's head. The artist of this sphinx (cat. no. 49) reduces the lion's naturally massive body to attenuated limbs which better suit the Egyptian taste for sleek, elegant lines. As usual, the figure wears the royal beard and had a crown which is now lost. The short curling tail is a modern restoration.

As in many ancient cultures, the Egyptians saw in the strongest and noblest of beasts a fitting symbol of royal power. By giving the lion a human head and a royal beard they made the identification even more explicit. The sphinx thus became the unambiguous embodiment of the king and is often shown in battle trampling on his enemies (cat. no. 30), or in three-dimensional sculpture as a benevolent guardian, reclining with the supreme grandeur that is so uniquely leonine. Thus sits the largest and most famous of all sphinxes watching over the great pyramids at Giza.

Small bronze statuettes like these were particularly popular in the Late Period, to which all three examples here belong. They were bought by worshippers and dedicated to the gods in temples as expressions of piety.

cat. no. **47**   cat. no. **48**   cat. no. **49**

Cat mummy

c.700–300 BC (Late Period)
Egypt (Saqqara?)
embalmed cat wrapped in linen
54.0 cm height
cat. no. 50

One of the strangest aspects of Egyptian religion was its apparent obsession with animals. Not only were many of the gods themselves conceived wholly or partly in animal form (see cat. nos 26, 35, 47, 48, 51), but each god and goddess was thought to hold some animal sacred, and the members of that species were regarded as manifestations of the deity. Since the gods were manifold, so too were their sacred beasts, and the Greek historian Herodotus exaggerated only slightly when he stated that among the Egyptians all animals 'both wild and tame are without exception held to be sacred'. Baboons and ibises were revered as incarnations of Thoth (cat. no. 51); Sobek was thought to infest waterways in the form of the crocodile; Horus glided across the skies as the falcon; and so on for almost every common species. Herodotus stated that the penalty for deliberately killing a sacred animal was death, and even an accidental casualty met with whatever punishment the priests saw fit. In some cults one particular animal was picked out on the basis of a special sign (usually its markings) and worshipped as the sole embodiment of that deity. Such was the Apis bull, venerated at Memphis as an aspect of the living Ptah, the great creator-god. An elaborate cult surrounded the Apis bull, and each time the existing incarnation died, the animal was carefully embalmed, mummified and buried in a huge sarcophagus with all the pomp and ceremony of a king.

In the Late Period (eighth to fourth centuries BC) animal cults became an increasingly conspicuous aspect of popular religion. The temple precincts must have come to resemble zoos, alive with screeching and squawking, as thousands of animals were kept by the priests as representatives of their respective gods. They were not kept just to be admired and pampered, however. Pilgrims would buy mummified animals for presentation to the appropriate deity. Literally millions of animal mummies have been found in huge underground burial chambers where they were interred at cult centres throughout Egypt. At Saqqara alone some four million ibises of Thoth have been found, carefully wrapped in linen and enclosed in clay pots, stacked from floor to ceiling in long underground galleries. An estimated 10 000 birds were buried there each year.

But probably the most popular of Egyptian animals was the cat, the sacred animal of the goddesses Bastet and Pakhet. Even domestic cats were treated with the greatest reverence, as Herodotus described:

> What happens when a house catches fire is most extraordinary: nobody takes the least trouble to put it out, for it is only the cats that matter: everyone stands in a row ... trying to protect the cats, who nevertheless slip through the line, or jump over it, and hurl themselves into the flames. This causes the Egyptians deep distress. All the residents of a house where a cat has died shave their eyebrows, and when a dog dies they shave the whole body including the head.

A number of cat-mummy cemeteries have been discovered, including one at Saqqara from which this example may have come. So numerous were the cat mummies at Beni Hasan that they were shipped to England by the tonne load last century to be turned into fertilizer. How this would have horrified the Egyptians, who, a Greek historian reported, lynched a Roman for accidentally killing a kitten!

Yet the ultimate fate of the sacred cats at the hands of the priests — after what was probably a short, if privileged, life — was hardly better. Animals selected for mummification had their necks broken and were then embalmed at the dedicator's expense. As with human corpses (see cat. no. 38), the internal organs were removed and the body dried in natron, a naturally occurring salt. The front legs were then drawn down the body and the back legs brought up against the pelvis for bandaging. Linen of different colours was often wrapped around the animal's body in careful layers to create geometric patterns on the mummy, with only the head popping out at the top. There, broader layers of cloth were made to adhere closely so that the form of the cat's face and ears would show. As a final touch, the features of the face were often painted in, and it is difficult to believe that their amusingly quizzical expressions were not intentional.

Dog-faced baboon

Statue representing a form of the
moon-god Thoth
after 30 BC (Roman Period)
Akhmim, Egypt
painted and gilded wood
39.0 cm height
cat. no. 51

The baboon was one of the Egyptians' favourite animals and large numbers of these exotic creatures were imported from Ethiopia and the Sudan from the beginning of pharaonic times. A baboon-god, known as 'the great White One', is attested already in texts from the Archaic Period and by the time of the pyramids he was regarded as a form of the moon-god Thoth, the inventor of hieroglyphs and the patron of scribes. All baboons were treated as sacred, and statues such as this served as cult images for worship.

A prayer to one such statue in the house of a scribe reads:

> Praise to thou, O lord of the house! Baboon radiant of mane, of sweet appearance and gentle charm, beloved of all men . . . That which is upon his head [the lunar crown] is of red jasper, and his phallus is cornelian. His love is poured out upon his eyebrows, and he opens his mouth to bestow life. My gateway is happy since Dog [i.e. Thoth] entered it; it has thrived and has been (richly) furnished from the time that my lord has trodden it . . . Thoth, thou shalt be my champion and I shall not fear the (evil) eye.

As always when he represents Thoth, the baboon is shown squatting. This is a natural posture for these animals, but the sedate and obedient way the hands are placed on the knees gives him an irresistibly human air. The peg at the top of the head originally secured a crown consisting of a moon-disc inside a crescent, an emblem of Thoth's lunar character. This association is echoed in the pendant on his chest which bears a wedjat, the Eye of Horus. In Egyptian mythology, the moon was thought to be the left eye of the falcon-headed sky-god Horus, which was brutally cut out by his evil uncle Seth. Thoth recovered the mutilated eye from the celestial ocean in a net and returned it to Horus, who used it to restore life to his dead father Osiris. The wedjat thus became a symbol of rejuvenation and protection against evil, and is one of the Egyptians' favourite designs for amulets and charms.

Large numbers of baboons were kept by the priests of Thoth, and by the priests of other deities associated with them. Far from being dumb animals, they were regarded as superior to man in their piety, which allowed them to converse with the gods, and in their greater understanding of sacred truths. The four baboons who sat on the sun-god's sacred boat are addressed as 'you who raise up truth to the Lord of All, who judge poor and rich, . . . who live on truth and gulp down truth, whose hearts have no lies, who detest falsehood'. The animals' screeching and running around at dawn was interpreted as an act of homage to the sun, and they are often shown in Egyptian art with their hands raised in reverence to the reborn solar disc (cat. no. 39). When the dead man is reborn in heaven he declares: 'I have hymned and worshipped the sun-disc, I have joined the worshipping baboons, and I am one of them'. One of the four Sons of Horus who protected the mummified organs of the body after death had the head of a baboon. And when sacred baboons died, they too were treated with great care and respect; after being embalmed and mummified they were buried in huge underground galleries in cemeteries devoted entirely to sacred animals.

The baboon's face has the dog-like muzzle that led the Greeks to call it the cynocephalus, or 'dog-headed' ape. Thick gilding creates a rich and dramatic effect. The eye — one is now missing — is a painted glass inlay.

cat. no. 51

Mummy-portrait of a woman

AD c.150–200 (Roman Period)
Er-Rubiyyat, Faiyum, Egypt
coloured wax on plastered wood
44.0 cm height
cat. no. 52

The woman in this portrait lived in Egypt in the second century AD, some two centuries after the country was first absorbed into the Roman Empire. She hardly *looks* Egyptian; her face, hairstyle, clothes and jewellery could be those of any well-to-do lady of the Mediterranean region. Nor does the style of the work betray its origin. Quite the opposite — the fresh, realistic approach could hardly be less like the stylized symbols of pharaonic art. And yet this woman believed in the transfigured after-life of the Egyptians and had her body embalmed in the age-old Egyptian manner. Indeed, this portrait was originally placed over the face of her mummy. Nothing illustrates better the meeting of cultures that took place in Hellenistic and Roman Egypt than this unlikely coming together of two of the most distinctive hallmarks of the Greco-Roman and Egyptian traditions: the portrait and the mummy.

Such cultural mixing represented a totally new phenomenon in Egypt, where, for the previous 3000 years, artists had stoutly resisted outside influence, inexorably turning out works according to the same basic stylistic formulas and drawing on the same basic reservoir of motifs and symbols. When foreigners overran the country — as Palestinians, Libyans and Nubians sometimes did — they inevitably adopted Egyptian customs and left the arts of the country essentially unchanged.

That is, until the arrival on the scene of Alexander the Great in 332 BC. Alexander opened Egypt to settlement by Greeks and other Hellenized foreigners, who were given privileged positions in the administration of the dynasty founded by his general, Ptolemy. Thus, for the first time, control of the country fell to a people who regarded their own culture as superior to that of the natives, and it was inevitable that the bastions of Egyptian cultural self-sufficiency would begin to crumble. The native religion, customs and

arts continued — the Ptolemies were careful not to offend local sensitivities — but they were now supplemented and modified according to Greek ways.

Chief amongst the new elements in Egyptian art was portraiture. Sculptors began to produce life-like studies whose depth of character and physiognomic realism goes far beyond earlier native experiments (cat. no. 43). In the first century AD (by which time control of Egypt had passed to the Romans) Egyptians of Greek and Roman descent began to have their mummies supplied with painted portraits. This practice reached a peak in the second and third centuries AD, and disappeared during the fourth century as the spread of Christianity led to the demise of mummification and other pagan burial rites. Although the Egyptians had for many centuries been placing stereotyped images of the deceased on coffins and mummy covers (see cat. nos 36, 37, 38, 39), the painted portraits of the Roman period seem to have belonged principally to Greeks and other culturally Hellenized groups. Native Egyptians by and large stuck to the traditional forms.

The woman of this portrait is shown as she would have appeared in life, wearing a shawl over a simple tunic, hoop ear-rings and a necklace of coloured stones — all standard Roman attire. Her hairstyle reflects the fashion first made popular by ladies of the imperial family in Flavian times, and in vogue for mummy-portraits throughout the second century AD. The gilt laurel wreath is the only overt funerary touch, an allusion to the happiness and grace of the hereafter.

Good mummy-portraits like this are full of character and convey a strong sense of individual likeness. The large doleful eyes, the careful modelling of the contours of the face by subtle gradations of colour and tone, and the judicious use of highlights — all combine to produce the plausible image of an attractive and dignified woman. Many different ethnic and facial types are represented in the hundreds of other surviving examples, reinforcing the impression that these are genuine portraits painted from life. And so some of them may have been,

commissioned while the subject was still in the full bloom of youth and originally hung like present-day portraits on living-room walls (one still has its frame and hanging string). Scholars believe, however, that most portraits were painted after death specifically for attachment to mummies, in which case their youthfulness — aged subjects are virtually unknown — must reflect artistic flattery. Like funerary art in many ages and cultures, people were represented not as they really were but as they or their descendants wished them to be remembered.

The medium of most portraits is beeswax, which was mixed with pigments and natron (a natural salt) and painted onto a plaster-coated wooden board. The wax creates a rich and luminous effect much like a modern oil painting. More than this, however, it was the wax's ability to survive in hot, dry conditions that appealed to the Egyptians. Scientific investigations have determined how the painting process worked, though some details are still not fully understood. The wax seems to have been applied in a liquid or creamy state with a brush. A blunt spatula-like instrument may also have been used on the face, where the wax was applied more thickly, giving a faint relief quality to the features. Pliny the Elder describes a very similar process used by Classical painters which he calls 'encaustic'.

This portrait, like most others, comes from the Faiyum oasis in northern Egypt, a rich agricultural area which was heavily settled in Greco-Roman times.

The Classical World: Greece and Rome

The millennium before the birth of Christ saw the political and cultural focus of the ancient world shift from the Near East and Egypt to the Mediterranean. While the Neo-Assyrians and Neo-Babylonians ruled the East, the small rugged land of Greece was emerging from four centuries of relative isolation into an era of renewed prosperity and innovation. Eager at first to learn as much as possible from their older Mediterranean neighbours, Athens and a handful of other prosperous city-states were, by the time of the Persian Empire, the centres of brilliant new developments in the arts, government and scientific thought — developments that gave Greek culture a direction and pace unparalleled in the East. The Greeks' pride in repelling a Persian invasion in 480–479 BC became a declaration of their keenly felt ethnic and cultural independence. A century and a half later, the triumph of the West was given political expression by Alexander the Great (336–323 BC), whose conquest of the Near East set the stage for the dissemination of Greek culture on a previously unthinkable scale. In the second century BC, Greece and the Hellenistic kingdoms of the East were absorbed in their turn into the empire of Rome — but a Rome increasingly imbued with Greek culture. Adding the Carthaginian domain to these territories, the Romans succeeded, where Alexander and his generals had failed, in welding the entire Mediterranean basin into a lasting political unity.

Of all the civilizations of the ancient world, Greece and Rome have played far the greatest role in shaping the form and character of Western civilization. Rediscovered and celebrated with renewed enthusiasm in the Renaissance, the Classical achievement has remained ever since an integral part of European culture, and through Europe of the 'Western' civilization which now spans the globe. Until recent times, Western art, architecture, literature, philosophy, mathematics and natural science — indeed virtually all creative and learned pursuits — traced their roots back to Greek and Roman soil, acknowledging the masters of Classical antiquity as models of excellence.

Even today philosophers may still begin their books with the theories of Plato, Aristotle or Lucretius; at school we learn the theorems of Euclid and Pythagoras; doctors still acknowledge the Hippocratic oath; and the works of literary giants like James Joyce and T.S. Eliot are woven around Classical tales and allusions.

Nowhere has Greco-Roman influence been more conspicuously pervasive than in the visual arts. It is a measure of this influence that, while Egypt and the Near East appear alien to modern eyes, the monuments of Greece and Rome often seem strikingly familiar. And for good reason. We have seen distant reflections of the Parthenon and Colosseum a hundred times over in the facades of our banks and museums; the works of sculptors from Michelangelo to Canova are fawning homages to the marbles of antiquity; and Roman portrait sculpture comes as no surprise after the toga-draped busts of eighteenth- and nineteenth-century Englishmen which still abound in antique shops today. The conscious break with tradition that characterizes most twentieth-century art has seen Classical principles recede further than ever before. But the Greco-Roman legacy remains part of the vocabulary of artistic change — a rich reservoir to be plundered from time to time for some evocative image, or perhaps just a convenient foil to be paraded as the epitome of outmoded values.

The central achievement of Greek art was figurative naturalism — the faithful replication of the human form as a vehicle for artistic expression. The shedding of arbitrary stylistic conventions did not of course mean the sudden end to any stylistic dimension in Greek art. But the variations in proportion, musculature, facial expression, hair and drapery by which style is gauged in Classical and later times are fine-tuning compared to the gross recasting of form and the unnatural imposition of patterning involved in Near Eastern and earlier Greek art.

Realism, the most extreme form of naturalism, is now so familiar a part of our artistic tradition that it is easy to forget how revolutionary a development it was. Diverging utterly from the priorities of Near Eastern art, naturalism also represented a reorientation from earlier Greek art, which, right to the brink of the Classical Period (c.480 BC), had been concerned as much with pattern and decoration as with fidelity to nature.

Greek figurative art begins to take shape in the Orientalizing Period of the seventh century BC, so named in recognition of the profound influence that Near Eastern ('Oriental') culture had on the nascent arts and crafts of Greece. The principal agents of Eastern contact were the Phoenicians of present-day Lebanon, who then dominated Mediterranean trade, plying the seas with shiploads of ivories, jewellery, metalwork and other richly decorated goods. Phoenician art was a very eclectic phenomenon, owing much of its style and content to other regions of the Near East. Trading their own products, Phoenician merchants were therefore trading a distillation of the Orient. This rich reservoir of exotic designs and subjects — particularly floral and animal motifs — proved an enormous stimulus to the artists of Greece (cat. no. 55), whose native geometric tradition rendered animate beings as little more than stick-figure silhouettes. In Etruria, too, Phoenician trade triggered an Orientalizing phase in the arts of the seventh and sixth centuries BC (cat. nos 56, 57).

The opening of Greek eyes to the East proved a crucial ingredient in the future development of Greek art, greatly supplementing the indigenous repertory of geometric designs and inspiring greater versatility in the handling of old themes. The interests Greek artists acquired in these years and the stylistic experiments they initiated led, in an uninterrupted development, through Archaic times to the Classical art of the fifth and fourth centuries BC. It is during this period that we first see evidence of the conspicuous pride in the human body — emphasized through the convention of heroic nudity — that lies at the heart of

The Greco-Roman World

BRITANNIA

Hadrian's Wall

Londinium

GERMANIA INFERIOR

Paris

Trier

Rhine R

GALLIA

BELGICA

GERMANIA SUPERIOR

Lyons

NORICUM

Aquileia

Nimes

Po R

Narbonne

Massilia

HISPANIA

Gades

CORSICA

Vulci

ETRURIA

SARDINIA

Rome

Pompeii

LATIUM

Tarentum

MAGNA GRAECIA

Rhegium

SICILY

Naxos

Syracuse

Carthage

MAURETANIA

NUMIDIA

Lepcis Magna

AFRICA

ILLYRICUM

DALMATIA

BALKANS

MOESIA

MACEDONIA

Thessaloniki

Pella

GREECE

Delphi

Olympia

Corinth

Athens

CRETE

Cyrene

CYRENAICA

Alexandria

EGYPT

Nile R

DACIA

Danube R

SCYTHIA

Chersonesus

BLACK SEA

Byzantium

Troy

ASIA MINOR

Smyrna

Sardis

Ephesus

Pergamum

RHODES

BITHYNIA AND PONTUS

Sinope

GALATIA

CAPPADOCIA

ARMENIA

LYCIA

CILICIA

Antioch

CYPRUS

Tyre

Enkomi

SYRIA

Damascus

Palmyra

Dura-Europos

MESOPOTAMIA

PARTHIANS

CASPIAN SEA

Tigris R

Euphrates R

Hatra

Seleucia

Ctesiphon

PERSIAN GULF

JUDAEA

Jerusalem

Naucratis

ARABIA PETRAEA

Petra

RED SEA

0   500km

later Greek art. The Greek alphabet, too, was a product of Eastern contact, copied from the Phoenician script in about 800 BC.

Closer attention to animate subjects gradually equipped Archaic artists to flesh out the stylized Orientalizing figures into more evocative representations of man in action and repose (cat. nos 62–65). But the process was certainly not a single-minded quest for figurative realism, an ideal Greek artists would not yet have acknowledged. Right to the end of Archaic times, the wilfully unanatomical stylization of muscles, hair and other features continued hand-in-hand with the emergence of a more plausible overall bodily form.

All this changed in the decades after 500 BC, which mark the dawning of the Classical Age. For the first time in the history of art, the desire to imitate nature — though always still a perfect, idealized form of nature — became artists' primary and now very conscious objective. And the remarkable fact is that they achieved this aim so successfully in the space of little more than twenty-five years, learning to imitate faithfully not only the surface contours of the body — the point at which Archaic art had arrived — but also the underlying structure and the way in which it is affected by stance and movement. By about the time of the Persian invasion of 480–479 BC, figures were being made which stood or moved in natural poses, achieving balance in the interplay of weights and stresses rather than the rigid symmetry of their sentry-like predecessors. Elements of stylization remained — especially in the treatment of faces and hair — but musculature, carriage and pose were now entirely plausible. Naturalism had arrived, and Western art would never be the same again.

The chief focus of interest in early Classical art was the male nude. Statues of women were by contrast largely excuses to explore the fall of drapery and the subtle suggestion of form underneath. To the fifth-century BC Greeks, the well-defined male physique represented nature's noblest form — the fitting mould in which to cast images of the gods, and the natural vehicle for

expressing the sublime in man. In Classical terms, the desire to perfect the representation of the athletic male was nothing less than the quest to perfect art itself.

But it was a selective and idealized naturalism, not an earthy realism, that artists sought. In gods and mortals alike the body is divested of irrelevant individuating features to yield a generalized image of the perfect athlete in the prime of early manhood. The face, too, though real enough in overall form, is not that of an individual, but of a godly ideal — the distilled essence of the noble, handsome visage. Every plane is smooth and regular, every feature perfectly formed and blemish-free; nowhere is there the slightest trace of a wrinkle or wart. The expression, devoid of emotion, projects a lofty serenity and otherworldliness, a state of ethereal detachment that belies the figure's often dramatic, even violent, actions.

Greek art's almost obsessive preoccupation with the human form is the most conspicuous aspect of a broader 'humanism' that suffuses Greek culture and sets it apart from all others. 'Man is the measure of all things', as one Greek philosopher put it, and this might almost have been the Greek credo. Placing man firmly at the centre of the universe, humanism was the lifeblood of Greek culture, both providing the impetus and giving focus to its extraordinary creative genius.

Belief in values defined according to human needs and responsibilities, and confidence in the power and authority of rational thought did not mean a repudiation of the gods. The Greeks were as god-fearing as any Eastern peoples. But it is symptomatic that they pictured their gods and goddesses, with few exceptions, in fully human form, and attributed to them the emotions and prejudices of ordinary men and women. Zeus, Athena, Apollo and the others were, in effect, humanity writ large.

The Greeks' talent for speculative thought manifested itself in philosophy and natural science in the novel assumption that observation and reason — man's ability to think things through — provided a sufficient

basis for divining the nature of things. The 'Socratic dialogue', in which the famous philosopher relentlessly exposes the presuppositions and inconsistencies of his interlocutor's thinking, set the pattern for subsequent philosophical inquiry — though not yet for his fellow Athenians: Socrates was executed for 'corrupting the youth'. The great playwrights of the fifth century BC — the redoubtable triad of Aeschylus, Sophocles, and Euripides — explored the human condition in more poetic but no less profound terms, dwelling particularly on the tragically flawed hero and man's ultimate impotence before the gods.

The Greek contribution to politics was nothing less than democracy itself. The Athenians invented the first government which gave adult males — women, foreigners and slaves could not vote — a direct role in the decision-making process, and ultimate jurisdiction over all government matters. Most contemporary philosophers regarded popular rule as volatile and misguided, but to Pericles it was the fairest and noblest system, and the modern world has generally agreed.

In 334 BC, Alexander the Great burst upon the ancient world like a whirlwind. Seven years later, still only twenty-nine years old, he had conquered all the known world from Greece to the borders of India. At a stroke, cultural and political boundaries which had existed for centuries were swept away. The diverse civilizations of Greece and Persia, Egypt and Afghanistan were brought briefly under one banner — a banner that, despite its nominally Macedonian colours, was essentially Greek. This vast empire fragmented soon after Alexander's early death, but he had changed forever the political complexion of the ancient world.

Although it was no part of his plan, Alexander was also the harbinger of a new era in Greek art. His wide-ranging conquests exposed artists to many new influences and changed forever the political and cultural conditions in which they worked. Currents of change which had been brewing in Greece in the fourth century BC were crystallized and given impetus by the political and cultural revolution he inaugurated. As horizons widened far beyond the Aegean, the focus of philosophical thinking began to shift from the virtues and needs of the state to those of the individual — and as more than just a citizen. Cross-fertilization between East and West saw Greek civilization transplanted as far afield as western India, and an influx of Eastern ideas and religious beliefs to the West. The division of Alexander's kingdom among his generals created an environment in which these and other forces in art were generously patronized, as the rival Hellenistic monarchs vied to outdo each other in the grandness of their courts.

A number of new interests and priorities emerged in Greek art of the Hellenistic Period in the wake of this political and cultural shake-up. The still predominantly idealizing athletic figures of the late Classical Period were supplemented by more honest and varied images of real people — young and old, thin and fat, Greek and foreign. This more graphic realism brought with it a belated recognition of facial expression, character and emotion, themes which lent Hellenistic art a newly dramatic dimension (cat. nos 84–86). These interests were now pursued in a number of provincial schools covering Egypt and the Near East as well as Greece and Italy.

In the third to first centuries BC, Rome gradually replaced the Hellenistic kingdoms as the major power in the Mediterranean. Greece, to which Rome already acknowledged a deep cultural debt, was treated with special tolerance; but in the second century BC, when continuing dissension forced the Romans to occupy the Aegean, there began the widespread pillaging that eventually saw hundreds of Greek sculptures and other moveable monuments shipped off to Rome, where they were greatly sought after by the rich and cultured. Workshops, mainly staffed by Greeks, arose to meet the demand for copies and adaptations of famous Greek masterpieces, many of which

are now known only through these imitations. One of the greatest of all admirers of Greek culture was the Emperor Hadrian (AD 117–138), whose villa at Tivoli outside Rome yielded three of the sculptures in this exhibition (cat. nos 68, 69, 86).

Roman views on the merits of Greek ways, especially their moral and philosophical values, were the subject of much debate during the last century of the Republic. But when Augustus finally brought an end to the political turmoil of these years and established himself as the first emperor (27 BC-AD 14), he had no hesitation in looking to Greece when formulating an imperial style in art. In what was clearly a conscious move, he settled upon the high Classical Style of Periclean Athens as the artistic vehicle which would best encapsulate the idealism and dignity he wished his portraits and other public monuments to project (cat. no. 88). The wholesale imposition of this quintessentially Greek style upon Roman state art crystallized and gave official sanction to the Hellenizing trends of the previous centuries. Augustan Neo-Classicism became fashionable also for portraits of the emperor's family (cat. nos 89, 90), and established a code which Roman state art would take as its point of departure for the next century.

If Roman culture is inconceivable without the Greeks, it is true also that the Romans pursued this legacy in new directions and broke much new ground of their own. Roman architects accomplished many unprecedented engineering feats; their writers and orators established new genres; and their artists drew on native Italic traditions in developing forms of expression which diverge markedly from their Greek counterparts. Of these last, the most conspicuous is portrait sculpture, which emerges in the last century of the Republic with a series of graphically realistic busts — probably inspired by the traditional Roman wax death-masks — which render in acute detail the age and character of their aristocratic subjects. We can well imagine in the more stern faces of this series the austere, pragmatic values of those reactionary

Romans who opposed the effete artfulness of the Greeks, and their images are indeed very different in spirit from Greek portraits of the Hellenistic Period (cat. no. 85). Hints of this coldly realistic style surfaced from time to time in later imperial portraits, and may even be detected in the Greek-looking Antoninus Pius (cat. no. 92). Non-Greek elements came increasingly to the fore in imperial art of the third and fourth centuries AD, but a florid Hellenistic style remained popular in luxury decoration (cat. no. 93).

The reign of Constantine the Great (AD 306–337) represents a turning point not only in Roman history but in the destiny of Western civilization as a whole. That the Western world is today largely Christian is due to the fact that Constantine adopted the new faith as the state religion of Rome, reversing three centuries of brutal opposition to this small, originally Jewish, sect. Paganism did not die overnight. Many retained their old beliefs and the old iconography was often reinterpreted rather than rejected outright (cat. no. 93). But as the forces of conversion gained momentum, the demise of an art so saturated with polytheism and the world of appearances could not long be averted. Byzantium, the Christianized Roman Empire, presided over the death of the Classical artistic tradition.

Greece (detail)

Mycenaean Greek bowl

1300–1200 BC, Late Bronze Age
(Mycenaean Period)
Enkomi, Cyprus
painted pottery
27.2 cm height

cat. no. 53

Throughout history, the island of Cyprus has been the meeting ground of East and West. In the Late Bronze Age (c.1550–1200 BC), when trade between the civilizations of the eastern Mediterranean was particularly intense, merchants were drawn to the island for its rich copper reserves, still at that time the staple metal for tools and weapons. Situated between European Greece and the Oriental civilizations of the Levant and Egypt, Cyprus also served as a natural staging post for merchants plying the seas between these markets, and Cypriot ports soon became flourishing emporiums where pottery, metalwork, ivories, jewellery and other goods from all over the eastern Mediterranean could be bought and sold. Fortunately for archaeologists, these imports were often buried with the dead, and by recording changes in the types and quantities of exotic goods it has proved possible to chart something of the island's changing political orientation and economic fortunes.

The involvement of the Greeks in Cyprus first becomes evident in the pottery. From about 1400 BC, an exceptionally finely made ceramic, with the distinctive shapes and painted decoration that any archaeologist immediately recognizes as Mycenaean (so called after the Greek site where it was first discovered), begins to appear in Cyprus in increasing quantities. As in Greece, it is mostly painted with plain bands or other simple geometric designs. But some vessels, like this one from Enkomi, carry elaborate pictorial scenes. More of this Pictorial Style has been found in Cyprus than in Greece itself, and while scientific tests on the clays of some Cypriot vases have shown that they came from Greece, others were probably made on the island by immigrant potters. When vessels as attractive as these were traded, it may have been for their own sake, not just as containers for wines, oils or perfumes (as was usually the case with undecorated wares).

Attempts have been made to identify particular Pictorial Style artists by their technical and stylistic quirks. According to these stylistic groupings, vases by the painter of the British Museum bowl (or perhaps the painter himself) travelled also to Greece. Of the six pots attributed to him, two (including this one) were found at Enkomi in Cyprus and three in Greece (the origin of the sixth piece is unknown).

The British Museum bowl is one of the finest and best preserved examples of the Pictorial Style that has survived. Greek pot-painters of the Late Bronze Age were not great artists, and their more elaborate figured scenes, though interesting as social and historical documents, usually consist of childishly incompetent stick-figures, chaotically arranged and poorly drawn. They were much better, as here, with a simple, bold design in which they could exploit a real talent for stylizing animals in dramatic and original ways. Much of the effect depends on filling the outline of the animal's body with repetitive geometric patterns. The result, executed in this piece with real confidence and flair, is a great decorative success.

Both sides show the same scene: a bull with head lowered charges at a bird, perhaps the cattle egret which feeds on parasites in bulls' hides. Although on one side the bird seems to be still engaged in this thankless service, the bull's galloping front legs leave no doubt that it is charging, and not just lowering its head for the bird to gain purchase. The rubber-like bending of the bull's legs is a device worthy of a cartoonist, so effectively does it convey the animal's movement — a very rare quality in this usually static art.

The vase was found in 1896 in British Museum excavations at Enkomi, near Famagusta, on the eastern coast of Cyprus. It came from a cave-like three-chambered tomb along with a number of other Mycenaean and local Cypriot pots of the thirteenth century BC.

cat. no. **53**

Phoenician-style bowl

c.800–700 BC (Orientalizing Period)
from a tomb at Sant'Angelo Muxaro, Sicily
gold
2.0 x 14.6 cm diameter
cat. no. 54

Of the peoples bordering the Mediterranean, none devoted themselves more enthusiastically to mastering the sea and exploiting its commercial opportunities than the Phoenicians of present-day Lebanon. Already in the Late Bronze Age (1550–1200 BC) their merchant venturers were taking a leading role in maritime trade, and by 700 BC Phoenician traders were calling at sites and establishing colonies the length and breadth of the Mediterranean basin. Some colonists even ventured beyond the 'Pillars of Hercules' (Straits of Gibraltar) and down the Atlantic seaboard as far as Mogador in modern Morocco. One colony at Carthage in northern Africa soon outstripped all the others, and eventually surpassed even the mother cities to become the foremost power and chief trading centre of the Phoenician world.

The eighth century BC, the highpoint of Phoenician settlement abroad, also marked the beginning of the Greek colonization of southern Italy and Sicily, which thereby became known as *Magna Graecia* (Greater Greece). As the influence and prosperity of these so-called Western Greeks grew, the Phoenicians were forced to compete for control of the lucrative maritime trade routes. In the carve-up of Sicily, the Carthaginians laid claim to the west of the island, the Greeks to the east, bringing the two cultures into direct and intimate contact. Despite the economic and political hostility which inevitably arose from such close and competitive cohabitation, Sicily (and southern Italy) became the scene of a fruitful intermingling of the Phoenician and Greek artistic traditions. Not only were Phoenician imports copied and adapted by the Western Greeks; some Phoenician craftsmen also settled in *Magna Graecia*, where their work is recognizable by its concessions to local tastes. Some of these immigrants no doubt instructed the local Greek and Italian craftsmen in their skills, and these pupils, being less wedded to Oriental ways, would modify and supplement the pure Phoenician style still more.

This magnificent gold bowl from Sicily has long been regarded as one of these Western creations, directly inspired by a Phoenician prototype. The basic form and decoration are well known from a series of bronze bowls decorated in low relief with rows of bulls. The Phoenicians were very fond of animal friezes, which normally had no particular religious significance. Here, however, we are reminded that bulls are the sacred animal of the Oriental moon-god, whose crescent is marked in punched dots. Phoenician 'bull bowls' were traded widely in the Mediterranean and the Near East in the ninth and eighth centuries BC. This is the only surviving example in gold, and the unusual style of the strangely emaciated bulls, with their prominent ribs and disproportionately large shanks, has led scholars to regard it as the creation of a Western Greek working in Sicily. That, in any case, is where it was found, along with an identical bowl and two other plain gold bowls, in about 1750. Judging by the pottery and other objects from burials at the site, its final owner was also a Western Greek.

The bowl is beaten from a single sheet of gold, to which were soldered the twisted wire rim and a row of tiny gold granules — a Phoenician speciality — around the central cavity. The relief bulls were produced with a punch applied to the back of the bowl, and the outlines then added by chasing. The central cavity would have been inlaid with a piece of coloured stone or glass, adding a splash of colour to the otherwise restrained relief decoration.

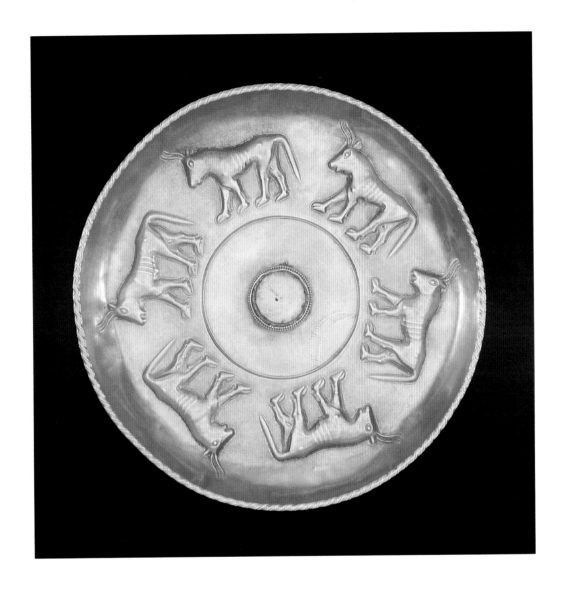

cat. no. 54

Greek jug in the Orientalizing Style

c.675 BC (Orientalizing Period)
Aegina, Greece; made in the Cyclades (Paros?)
painted pottery
41.5 cm height
cat. no. 55

Most of the Eastern objects imported to Greece in the Orientalizing Period (late eighth and seventh centuries BC) were small precious items such as jewellery, ivories and decorated metal vessels. As well as copying these objects in the same materials, Greek craftsmen also translated their designs to other media, particularly the painted decoration on pottery, adapting them in the process to their own tastes and requirements. The elegantly stylized Oriental animal and floral motifs were supremely decorative and had an obvious appeal to Greek artists, whose native tradition rendered animate beings as little more than sketchy, ill-proportioned stick figures. Here, on the other hand, was a fascinating menagerie of exotic creatures which sparked the imagination and opened up a whole new world of decorative possibilities.

Chief amongst the exotic novelties introduced to the Greek artistic repertory at this time were floral designs based on the lotus-bud and palm (neither native to Greece) and various animals, both real beasts and mythical composites such as griffins (eagle-headed, winged lions) and sphinxes (woman-headed, winged lions). Some of these imaginary beasts had been adopted from the East by Mycenaean Greeks in the Bronze Age. But they later vanish, and the versions which reappear in the Orientalizing Period faithfully copy the distinctive details of the new forms then current in Phoenicia, Syria and Anatolia. The Greeks were also inspired to create new hybrids of their own, such as the half-man half-horse centaur.

The British Museum jug is an exceptionally well preserved example of the Orientalizing Style current in the Greek islands around 675 BC. It is intact except for minor damage to the ears. The hatched and blacked-in geometric designs around the animals are legacies of the Geometric Style, but otherwise everything has an unmis-takably Oriental flavour, from the griffin-head spout to the painted animal and floral designs. A half century earlier, Oriental lions had been blacked out in good Geometric Style; now more concessions are made to the Oriental manner of painting in a combination of silhouette and outline, with stippling and other internal patterning. The details of the griffin — its forehead 'warts', horse's ears, muzzle-like lower beak and band of mane around the jaw — betray its ultimately Syrian (Neo-Hittite) source of inspiration. These strange beasts originally came to Greece on large bronze cauldrons bearing series of sculpted griffins' heads around their rims.

Lions had probably been hunted out in Greece by this time, but they still roamed the Near East, where they were often shown, as on this jug, attacking their prey. Grazing animals, especially rows of goats and stags extending right around the vessel, were particularly popular on the 'East Greek' pottery of Miletus in western Turkey. In the Cyclades and on the mainland they take a back seat to the main action scenes, as the grazing horses here are relegated to the side panels.

The rows of triangles topped by palmettes and scrolls near the bottom of the jug are another Eastern motif which was later used, following Oriental practice, as the design for column capitals in stone. These so-called Aeolic capitals were popular in Greece in the seventh and sixth centuries BC, after which the more familiar Doric and Ionic orders took over.

cat. no. 55

Etruscan jewellery

Necklace
c.700–600 BC (Orientalizing Period)
Italy (?), findspot unknown
glass and gold
face pendant 3.1 cm height
cat. no. 56

Disc ear-ring (one of a pair)
c.530 BC (Orientalizing Period)
Italy (?), findspot unknown
gold
6.1 cm diameter
cat. no. 57

Myrtle wreath
c.300 BC (Hellenistic Period)
Italy (?), findspot unknown
gold
27.9 cm length (inner curve)
cat. no. 58

'Tuscany', the modern name of the region north of Rome, still betrays the identity of its ancient inhabitants, the Etruscans, who lived there from about 700 BC. According to Herodotus, they came to Etruria — as the Romans called it — from Lydia in western Turkey, a view supported by the presence of Eastern elements in their arts and crafts. Many other aspects of Etruscan culture, however, have local roots, and despite much discussion their origins remain an open question.

The heyday of Etruscan civilization was the seventh and sixth centuries BC, before the Romans had begun to flex their military muscle beyond the seven hills of Rome. The Etruscans had their own distinctive language — which is still not fully understood — and developed a highly sophisticated culture, most celebrated today for its tomb paintings, terracotta sculptures and jewellery. But Italy was also the scene of intense competition between the Phoenicians and Greeks over trade routes and sites for colonies, and the presence of these foreigners inevitably left its mark. Eastern artefacts brought by Phoenician merchants inspired the Orientalizing Style which, as in Greece, dominates the arts of Etruria in the seventh and sixth centuries BC. Later it was principally the artwork of the Western Greeks, who then occupied much of southern Italy and Sicily, which the Etruscans imported, imitated and adapted.

Both currents of influence can be seen in this selection of Etruscan jewellery. Actual Phoenician imports (not local copies) are the multicoloured glass beads and face pendant of the glass and gold necklace (cat. no. 56). Glasswork was a Phoenician speciality and these beads are found wherever their trading-ships called. Here the Etruscan jeweller has combined them with gold beads decorated in filigree (fine gold wire) and granulation (patterns of tiny gold granules). The extensive use of these techniques was one of the hallmarks of Etruscan jewellery. Their effect in the necklace is quite tame, but later pieces, like the sixth-century BC disc ear-ring (cat. no. 57), are real *tours de force* of unrestrained granulation. This technique, too, the Etruscans first saw on Phoenician imports, but they soon mastered it themselves and pushed the method to new limits of technical and decorative sophistication, which have rarely been surpassed since. Figurative elements, like the rosettes and three lions' heads in this disc, serve as little more than bases for the elaborate patterns of fine wire and granules. One of a pair (the other now lost), this disc alone carries hundreds of tiny gold granules, each only a fraction of a millimetre across. The most elaborate pieces have thousands of granules, as little as 0.14 millimetres in diameter. The combination of such phenomenal craftsmanship with the Etruscans' refined sense of decoration makes their early jewellery among the most lavish and delicate in antiquity.

After the fifth century BC, from which very little evidence has survived, Etruscan jewellery experienced something of a renaissance in the fourth and early third centuries BC. It was Greek models that were now emulated, as in the wreath of myrtle leaves and berries (cat. no. 58). In Greece, wreaths of leaves were given as prizes in athletic and musical competitions. Gold wreaths were offered by the state to honour public figures. They were also worn in religious processions, dedicated in temples and buried with the dead. It is to this last custom that we owe the wreaths that survive today. Most are very flimsy affairs that could not have been worn, but this is one of the rarer sturdy examples which may have been used in life.

In all periods, Etruscan jewellers tended to avoid the use of colourful glass, gems and enamel that so attracted the Phoenicians and Hellenistic Greeks. For them, jewellery was essentially a matter of goldwork pure and simple, and decoration relied upon the skilful manipulation of this most sumptuous and uncorruptible of materials.

The ear-ring was attached by pushing a narrow tube that projects from the centre of the back through the ear. To keep it from falling off, a chain (now lost) running from the edge of the disc could be attached to the looped end of the tube.

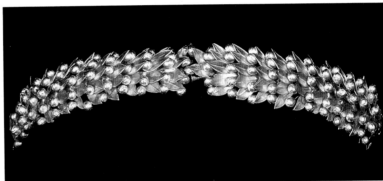

cat. no. 57   cat. no. 58   cat. no. 56

Greek and Roman jewellery

Greek plaques showing a winged goddess
(Artemis?) and lions; probably worn as a pectoral
c.650–625 BC (Orientalizing Period)
Camirus, Rhodes, Greece
gold
4.2 cm height
cat. no. 59

Greek diadem with knot of Heracles
c.300–200 BC (Hellenistic Period)
Greece (Melos?)
gold, enamel and garnet
27.9 cm length
cat. no. 60

Roman bracelet in the form of a coiled snake
c.AD 1–100 (Early Imperial Period)
findspot unknown
gold
8.2 cm diameter
cat. no. 61

To the ancients, no less than today, gold was a by-word for wealth and status. When a Greek described the filthy rich, he naturally did so in terms of gold. Prized for its seemingly magical resistance to corrosion, this most precious of all metals was crafted by the best metalsmiths and jewellers of the day, and their products represent not only extraordinary technical feats but also some of the most outstanding works of decorative art from antiquity.

Most of Greece's gold was imported from the East. Some came in the form of finished artefacts, and it was largely through this trade — along with imports of bronzework, ivories, gems and textiles — that Near Eastern patterns and themes were adopted into the Greek artistic tradition during the eighth and seventh centuries BC. The islands of the Aegean, as the first landfalls for ships sailing from the East, were exposed to the full force of these Orientalizing winds. Most of the gold was melted down and reworked, but pieces such as the series of plaques (cat. no. 59) from Rhodes, the easternmost of the Greek islands, show that some of the finished imports were imitated in local work.

The winged female figure on each plaque derives from the ancient Semitic goddess of fertility and war, Astarte, infamous from the Bible as the idol of wayward Israelites. She is shown in the classic Near Eastern attitude as 'mistress of animals', flanked by lions (an Eastern animal) which she holds by the backs of their heads. Plaques showing the goddess in this and similar attitudes were apparently a speciality of the Rhodian jewellers. At the bottom are suspended a row of pomegranates, another Oriental symbol of fertility associated with Astarte.

The goddess here is still very close to her Near Eastern prototype: the 'Daedalic' face (so-named after the mythical Greek craftsman of the labyrinth of King Minos), with ample hair falling in strict layers to the shoulders, can be closely matched on carved ivories from Phoenicia. But she was soon modified according to Greek taste; for the islanders rarely copied foreign works exactly, preferring to select those features which suited their purpose, and adapting these to produce an art which can claim much originality of its own. Eventually, Oriental Astarte became Greek Artemis, the virgin goddess, 'queen and huntress chaste and fair', who reigned over the animal kingdom. At this early stage, however, it is hard to say precisely which deity the Greek artist imagined himself to be representing. At Ephesus in western Turkey (a region then populated by Greeks) Artemis long retained her Oriental associations with fertility, and is shown in Greco-Roman sculpture with what appear to be numerous egg-like breasts, but may in fact be rows of bulls' scrota strung around her chest.

The raised figures on the plaques were formed by hammering the gold sheets over a matrix of some hard material. Details were skilfully rendered by granulation and filigree, techniques which were also adopted at this time from the East. The series of plaques was probably worn as a pectoral strung across the chest.

Alexander the Great's capture of the great Persian treasuries in the late fourth century BC produced an unprecedented glut of gold in the Greek world. One result was a renaissance in Greek jewellery, invigorated by renewed contact with Eastern art. Control of the Oriental trade routes also made available a variety of exotic stones, and jewellery of the Hellenistic Period, like the diadem from Melos (cat. no. 60), is therefore more colourful than ever before. Alexander the Great had taken to wearing the Persian diadem as a symbol of his own kingship, and later Hellenistic kings continued to tie diadems around their heads as a mark of royalty. Decorative versions in metal, like this piece, were worn also by their more well-to-do subjects.

The 'knot of Heracles', which forms the diadem's central design, was a popular innovation of the period. Its vogue again stems from Alexander, who claimed descent from Heracles and thus came to be identified with the double knot by which the legendary hero secured the Nemean lion skin at his throat. By association with Heracles' marriage to Deianeira, it also became a popular device on women's jewellery. As an evocative symbol of the mighty hero's strength and fecundity — he had some seventy children — the double knot was commonly used in the decoration of marriage belts.

The Romans of the Republican Period, reacting against the extravagant ways of their Greek and Etruscan neighbours, at first took a very dim view of all jewellery and other outward displays of wealth. Wearing gold rings was long forbidden to all but certain classes of nobles, government officials and military heroes. A law passed in the third century BC limited the amount of gold a woman could wear to fourteen grams. But, as in other areas of life, this Republican austerity eventually broke down, and Roman women of the Imperial Period were in practice restrained only by their modesty and their husbands' generosity. To judge by St Paul's comments about Roman ladies' lavish jewels, this did not inhibit them very much.

The solid gold snake bracelet (cat. no. 61), dating to the first century AD, derives from the popular Greek serpent bracelets, which were in turn influenced by earlier Oriental designs. Like much Roman jewellery, it is competently crafted but lacks the sophistication and refinement of the best Greek work.

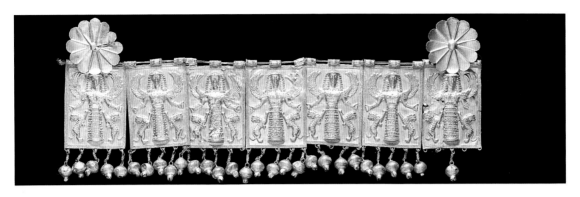

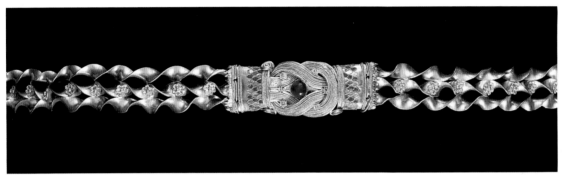

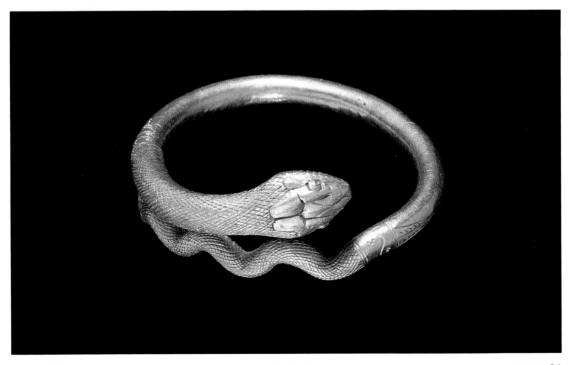

cat. no. 59   cat. no. 60   cat. no. 61

Greek mounted warrior

c.550 BC (Archaic Period)
southern Italy (Armentum?); probably made in
Rhegium or Tarentum
bronze, solid cast
23.6 cm height
cat. no. 62

For five centuries after the end of the Bronze Age, when Greek pottery reverted to purely geometric decoration, it was principally in the casting of small bronzes (and poorer quality works in stone and terracotta) that figurative art survived. Here, too, the geometricizing spirit of the period made itself felt: men and animals become stiff, stick-like symbols, devoid of the naturalism which had breathed life into Minoan and Mycenaean art. But a tradition of figurative sculpture was at least kept alive until the seventh century BC, when monumental stone sculpture of an entirely different kind took root (see cat. no. 65).

The Greeks always prized sculpture in bronze more highly than that in marble, and some of the best work continued to be seen in the small bronzes intended for temple dedications and private display. One of the finest to have survived from any period is this mounted warrior, dating to around 550 BC. The maritime fringe of southern Italy, where it was found, had been heavily colonized by the Greeks from the late eighth century BC, and the culture of this Greater Greece (*Magna Graecia*), as it became known, was therefore thoroughly Hellenic. Inevitably, however, the arts of the colonies gradually diverged from the homeland and absorbed aspects of the indigenous Italian cultures. This statuette is still essentially in the Greek tradition, but it has features which mark it unequivocally as Italian.

Although there was no true cavalry in Archaic Greece, some of the infantry would ride to the battlefield on horseback. Thus our warrior was originally shown fully kitted-up for battle, with a spear in his left hand and a shield on his right arm, which also held the reins. All these more delicate parts have been destroyed. He wears a short, belted tunic (*chiton*), which affords no protection to his body and leaves his masculinity — rendered with an exaggerated prominence that is typically south Italian — fully exposed. His only armour is a helmet, which had its crest (also lost) running sideways.

The sprightly walking horse is a masterpiece of elegant stylization. Judiciously reducing the animal's body to a series of smoothly rounded volumes and flowing lines, the sculptor skilfully effects a very satisfying simplification of the natural forms without in any way diminishing the sense of animation: the horse is as much alive and in motion as many a Classical Greek mount. He devotes special care to the form and articulation of the hoofs — they are the most naturalistic part of the animal — for it is in these that the sense of movement resides. The stiff front legs, prominent chest and high head are also emphasized, conveying well the proud, noble spirit which so endeared this animal to the Greeks.

The controlled stylization of works like this is a vivid reminder that Greek art was not driven solely by the desire to achieve ever more realistic effects, as a concentration on later periods can sometimes make it seem. The attempt to copy nature was only one of many guiding principles in early Greek art, and for a long time a relatively minor one. Our sculptor — working less than a century before the first Classical sculptures — has not tried to imitate nature; on the contrary, he deliberately transmutes a natural subject into simpler, more elegant forms. He is as much concerned with pleasing patterns as with anatomical fidelity: the horse's body is rather too long and the eyes too large; the hair of the mane falls in unnaturally regular strands, swept around the ears for dramatic effect; and the rump muscles become the basis of an abstract engraving which no longer reflects any anatomical reality. In all this, naturalism is pursued only to the extent that it contributes to the artist's essentially decorative aims — an aesthetic closer in many ways to that of the Achaemenid Persians (see cat. nos 14, 16) than to Greek art of the Classical and Hellenistic Periods. What connects it to later Greek art is the incipient sense of structure and movement.

In Archaic times horse ownership was an important economic status-marker, and in some states even constituted the qualification for admission to an elite socio-political class — the 'knights'. This statuette was probably dedicated in a sanctuary by one such member of the southern Italian aristocracy. Recent research suggests that it was found at Armentum in Lucania, but where in southern Italy it was made remains uncertain. Tarentum (modern Taranto), at this time the major city of the region, and Rhegium (where the Chalcidian rose-bud decoration on the helmet would be more at home) have been suggested.

The warrior and horse were cast separately using the lost-wax technique. Both are solid; the more difficult hollow-casting method was not yet in common use. A division can be seen half-way up the horse where a second pouring of molten metal began.

Greek vase by Exekias

Achilles killing Penthesilea (obverse) and
Dionysus and Oinopion (reverse)
c.540–530 BC (Archaic Period)
Vulci, Italy; made in Athens, Greece
painted pottery (Athenian black-figure ware)
41.5 cm height
cat. no. 63

Vase painting in antiquity was not in general a high art form. Its practitioners — many of them potters as well as painters — were craftsmen rather than artists, producing large quantities of relatively inexpensive wares; in Classical times a large painted vessel cost only about a day's wage. Occasionally, however, a vase painter emerged who managed to elevate his craft above this secondary role as a 'minor' and essentially decorative art to the point where it may bear comparison with sculpture and what little we know of the other major representational arts: metalwork and wall-painting.

One such figure is Exekias, probably the finest of all Athenian black-figure vase painters. He was active around 540–530 BC, a relatively short painting career (though he seems to have continued potting for longer) which corresponds to the last years of rule of the tyrant Peisistratus. It was under Peisistratus and his sons that Athens became the leading artistic centre of Greece — a pre-eminence previously held by Corinth, the islands and eastern Greece — and began to export pottery widely.

The black-figure technique in which Athenian pottery of Exekias' day was decorated had been invented in Corinth around 700 BC, but the Athenians soon made it their own, far outstripping all other ceramic centres in the quality and interest of their compositions. In this technique the figures were first painted as silhouettes, and the outline and internal details then incised with a sharp point. Matt white paint was used for women's flesh and sparingly for other details of dress and weapons, where purple was also employed. The vessel was then baked, the amount of oxygen in the kiln being carefully controlled so that the background clay would turn matt orange or red, and the painted areas a glossy black. The final effect

was in many ways closer to certain kinds of figured metalwork than to wall-painting, and decorated vessels of bronze, silver and gold — which unfortunately rarely survived the melting pot — may indeed have been a major source of inspiration to Archaic pot-painters in the composition of their scenes.

The British Museum vase is one of Exekias' great masterpieces. The principal scene shows Achilles, the hero of the Trojan War, locked in battle with Penthesilea, Queen of the Amazons, a wild tribe of warrior women who had come to the Trojans' aid. Blood gushes out as the Athenian hero thrusts his spear into the queen's neck, tragically falling in love with his victim (so legend had it) as their eyes met at the very instant of death. The queen, as mistress of animals, wears a panther skin over her fine tunic.

The other scene is by contrast peaceful and relaxed: the wine-god Dionysus holding sprays of ivy, his sacred plant, and lifting to his lips a wine cup which his son Oinopion has filled from a jug.

Exekias was a masterful draughtsman with an acute sense of detail. He lavished great care on the fine details of clothing and other attributes of the figures (here, on Penthesilea especially), and on the subsidiary decoration. The series of meticulously drawn spirals below the handles, the perfectly regular ivy leaves held by Dionysus, and the floral and geometric designs on the neck and base of the vase show the steady hand of a most accomplished technician.

But it is in the dignity and emotional gravity with which Exekias managed to imbue his subjects that his real genius lay, separating him so emphatically from his contemporaries. He skilfully selected for portrayal the moment most highly charged with emotion and tragedy. Sometimes this is a point of high action and drama, as in this work, when, in the instant of irreparable loss, Penthesilea's death is made more tragic by the fleeting love it inspires. But elsewhere, in a totally new departure, Exekias depicted the moment before or after the dramatic deed: Ajax pensively securing the sword onto which he would

impale himself, rather than the gory act itself.

Despite the still somewhat formulaic drawing conventions of the day — the gestures are dramatically mannered and the rendering of drapery and muscles still somewhat schematic — Exekias imbued his figures with an inner life which began to turn the stiff dummies of Archaic art into evocative characters. The combatants' piercing stares (exaggerated by the conventional practice of showing the eyes of profile faces frontally, giving them a disturbingly obsessive glare) and the more subtle but equally effective hand gestures of Oinopion and Dionysus relate the figures psychologically, just as the tight, two-figure grouping of Achilles and Penthesilea unites them in composition. Isolated here in statuesque pairs, his figures acquire a monumentality and presence far beyond their actual scale.

As was common practice in heroic or mythological scenes, all the figures have their names written beside them. Exekias also signs the vessel as potter (*EXEKIAS EPOIESE*, 'Exekias made (me)'); though he does not say so here, he was no doubt the painter too. Beside Penthesilea he writes 'Onetorides is beautiful', a common way of paying a compliment to a popular boy in a society where homosexuality was widely considered a natural part of male development.

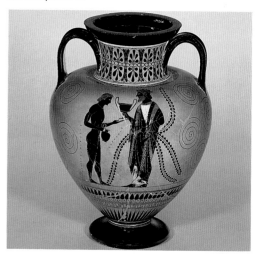

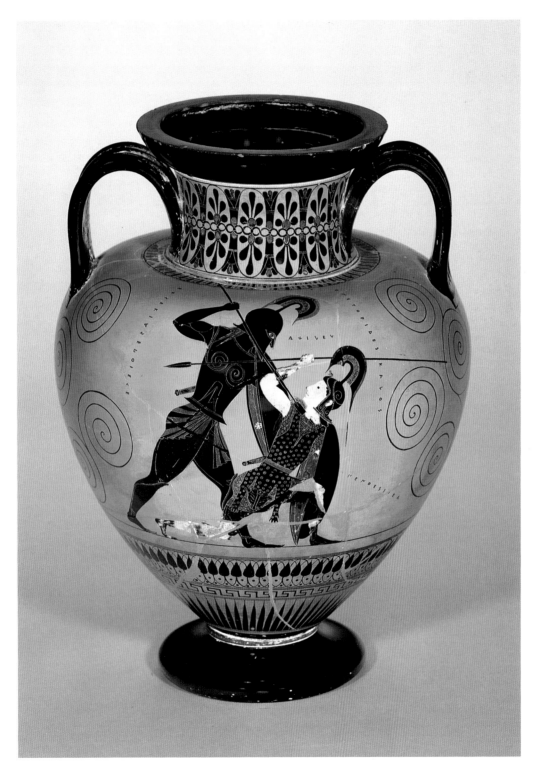

cat. no. 63

Greek wine jar

Warriors (obverse) and Dionysus with
attendants (reverse)
c.525–500 BC (Archaic Period)
Vulci, Italy; made in Athens, Greece
painted pottery (Athenian red-figure ware)
63.0 cm height

cat. no. 64

In about 530 BC an Athenian vase painter invented a new technique which was to revolutionize his art. Red-figure painting, as the name implies, was a complete reversal of the old black-figure ware (see cat. no. 63). Instead of painting the figures in black, they were now reserved in red (the natural colour of the fired clay) and the background was blacked in. This light-on-dark technique made for a more natural effect than the old-style silhouettes, and allowed details of anatomy and dress to be painted in, rather than having to be incised through the black paint, as before. The greater fluidity of line which the brush made possible did much to encourage the growing interest in naturalism.

The generation of painters who invented and popularized this technique in the last decades of the sixth century BC are aptly known as the 'Pioneers'. This vase is a beautifully fresh and well preserved work of the period, by an artist whose work shows a close familiarity with the so-called Euergides Painter, perhaps by that artist himself.

One side shows a hoplite warrior, named by the accompanying inscription as an otherwise unknown Hippaichmos, with his horse and a Scythian archer. Although there was no true cavalry corps at this time in Greece, those of the infantry wealthy enough to own a horse would often ride to the battlefield on horseback. The warrior is shown here in the usual battle dress, protected by a shield, greaves (shin armour), corselet (obscured by the shield) and helmet, and bearing a thrusting spear, the main offensive weapon of the day. He has probably just dismounted and is handing the reins to his Scythian companion, named Serague. Such Scythians — instantly recognizable by their gaily patterned costumes, tall leather hats and bows — were semi-nomads, originally from southern Russia, who came into contact with the Greeks around the shores of the Black Sea (see cat. no. 18). They first appeared on the streets of Athens under the Peisistratid tyranny and became something of a fad on late sixth-century vases. Scythian archers were employed as a police force in fifth-century Athens, but their novelty had evidently worn off by then, and they all but disappear from vases after about 490 BC.

The other side of the vase shows the wine-god Dionysus, a favourite subject on wine jars and cups, represented here holding a drinking-cup and vine, and attended by a satyr and maenad. Satyrs, perennial favourites of Archaic and later Greek art, were mythological man-horse hybrids with a human body, the tail and ears of a horse, and a snub-nosed, bestial face. Despite this gross appearance, they were engagingly mischievous creatures with an unabashed (and all too human) weakness for wine, women (maenads would do nicely!) and song — tastes they are often shown freely indulging in the company of their patron deity. The one here is named Briachos. Maenads, despite their seductive appearance, could be more menacing. Dancing in Dionysus' troop, they were prone to work themselves to such a pitch of mystical frenzy that they would run through the mountains tearing living creatures limb from limb and eating their raw flesh. Here Erophyllis, as she is named, holds a snake, symbol of the dark powers of the underworld, and a staff entwined with ivy, the maenads' usual totem.

Painted within a few decades of Exekias' masterpiece (cat. no. 63), the interests of a new generation are here beginning to show. The red-figure technique immediately imbues the figures with a lightness and luminosity which evokes infinitely more life than the grand master's silhouettes. The drawing, too, has advanced through closer attention to nature. Men's thighs have lost their unnatural massiveness and drapery falls more freely, though still clinging as if soaking wet to the buttocks and backs of the legs. Difficult twisting poses and sharply angled views of limbs were at this time the subject of much attention and competition. Our artist, though not among the avant-garde, copes well with the satyr's almost profile torso; the horse's diminutive frontal head, on the other hand, connects rather uncomfortably with its neck. Exekias' static, theatrical gestures have loosened up into something approaching a sense of continuing movement: the warrior walks convincingly, and there is real spring in the satyr's step. His somewhat over-defined knees and muscles are a symptom of early naturalism's preoccupation with accurate observation of anatomical detail. Later artists would learn to convey as much and more with fewer, well-chosen lines (cat. no. 66). As in earlier Archaic art, decoration still plays a major role. Much care is taken over the decorative palmette and vine-leaf borders, and with the more decorative aspects of the figured scenes: the splashes of purple for selected details, and the thick globules of paint which give an almost sculptural quality to Dionysus' grapes.

Like much of the Greek pottery in museums today (see also cat. nos 63, 66), this vase was found not in Greece but in Italy. It comes from Vulci in Etruria, where it had accompanied a wealthy Etruscan to his grave, probably containing wine. Desired for its exoticism as well as its superior finish and artistry, such pottery seems to have been placed in Italian burials as a respectable substitute for the family silver, something even wealthy aristocrats were reluctant to see consigned to oblivion with their forebears. From the late Archaic Period on, a significant proportion of Athenian pottery production was directed to this western export market, where many vessels served purely as funerary offerings. This wine jar is a shape which was particularly popular in the decades around 500 BC.

cat. no. **64**

Greek *kouros*

The 'Strangford Apollo'
c.500 BC (Late Archaic Period)
Greece, reportedly from the island of Anaphe
marble
1.01 m height
cat. no. 65

The enduring preoccupation of Greek art with the human form is nowhere more apparent than in the earliest life-size stone sculpture. The small bronzes of the Geometric Period had seen a fair quotient of animals and demons; but when, from about 630 BC, the Greeks began to carve full-size marbles, the vast majority of early works were figures of themselves, or of their gods in human form: standing male nudes, known after the Greek terms as *kouroi* (youths), and draped females or *korai* (maidens). (The singular forms are *kouros* and *kore* respectively.)

The inspiration for large stone statuary came from those masters of scale, the Egyptians. The Greeks had long enjoyed intermittent trade with Egypt and, around the time they began to produce the first large works, groups of mercenaries and merchants had begun to settle in the Nile Delta. There they were able to see the grand monuments of this ancient civilization first-hand, an experience which seems to have stimulated their first experiments with life-size stone statuary back home. Coming fairly late in the Orientalizing Period of Greek art, the inception of the *kouros* sequence represents one of the few direct Egyptian legacies to Greek art.

The conventional Egyptian stance of the standing pharaoh or deity was adopted almost unchanged for the Greek *kouros*: rigidly upright with the weight evenly distributed on both feet, the left leg advanced, hands by the sides with fists clenched (Egyptian figures often held a short baton), the head facing directly forward. This sentry-like straitjacket, giving most *kouroi* a formal, soulless character, was maintained for almost a century and a half.

As was so often the case with the Greeks, however, they adapted the foreign type to their own tastes and interests. From the beginning, male clothing was dispensed with: the *kouros*, unlike the pharaoh, always confronts the world in a state of 'heroic nudity'. Hairstyles, faces and other details of the Greek figures also are un-Egyptian. Indeed, in everything other than stance, the dramatic transformation that the *kouros* underwent in the century and a half of its existence quickly eradicated all trace of Egyptian descent. This extraordinary metamorphosis — ultimately giving rise to the first truly naturalistic three-dimensional image of man in the history of art — is one of the chief yardsticks by which the transition from Archaic to Classical art is traced.

The Strangford *kouros* (so named after its nineteenth-century owner) stands near the end of this sequence on the threshold of full naturalism. The first *kouroi* were highly stylized works with unnaturally tall heads, narrow waists and a simplified formula of patterned grooves and swellings for muscles and tendons. These proportions were calculated on an Egyptian schema which divided the figure into twenty-one equal units. As the sixth century progressed, the relative dimensions of body parts were made to approximate more closely to reality, and the surface contours of muscles and bone structure loosened up. In the Strangford *kouros* these developments are approaching a plausible image of the human form. The proportions are close enough to those of a well-developed male physique; and while the flat, squared stomach muscles still owe as much to geometry as anatomy, the chest and legs are keenly observed and carefully modelled. And the face has lost the incongruous 'Archaic smile' with which earlier figures innocently confronted the world.

Yet despite this progress, the Strangford *kouros* is locked into the same stiff, uncompromisingly frontal stance as his predecessors. The four-square pose still mirrors the Archaic method of working inwards from a drawing on each side of a rectangular block; the figure is still a symbol rather than a convincing image, a formula of noble manhood rather than the representation of an individual. He fails to evoke any potentiality of movement, or even the suggestion that another posture could have been adopted. This last vestige of the Archaic spell, inherited from Egypt, was not finally broken until the time of the Persian Wars, around 480 BC.

Like most Greek sculptures, this *kouros* would originally have been painted in something approaching natural colours. Following Egyptian practice, the flesh areas of the earliest *kouroi* were painted a deep red or brown, but by the time of the Strangford *kouros* a more subtle skin tone was preferred. Darker colours were used for all hair, the eyes, lips and nipples. Freshly painted, the polychrome effect of these statues must have been quite dazzling. Coloured replicas look quite 'unclassical' to the modern eye, accustomed as we are to the purity of the plain white marble. But to the Greeks the addition of colour was an essential ingredient of artistic mimicry.

Most *kouroi* have been found in sanctuaries, especially shrines of Apollo. It is for this reason that the Strangford Apollo and other pieces were originally identified as cult images of the god. In fact, however, they were probably worshippers' offerings, expressions of vigilant service to the god by the dedicator. Others were placed as markers above graves, sometimes engraved with the name of the deceased. These funerary *kouroi* were not in any way portraits, however: boys and old men alike are represented as idealized heroes in the prime of early manhood.

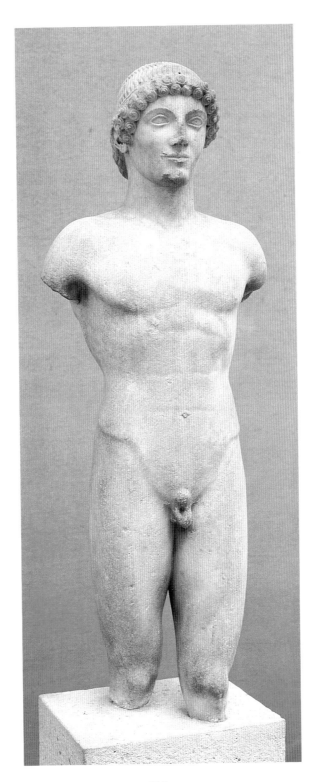

cat. no. 65

Greek wine jar by the Berlin Painter

Youth carrying wine jar (obverse) and man
playing lyre with dog (reverse)
c.480 BC (Early Classical Period)
Vulci, Italy; made in Athens, Greece
painted pottery (Athenian red-figure ware)
57.2 cm height

cat. no. 66

The Berlin Painter (so-called because one of his vases is in a museum there) was arguably the finest vase painter of his generation and ranks among the all-time Athenian greats. His speciality involved placing isolated figures, or small overlapping groups, on a plain black background. Here we see two revellers, a young man carrying a wine jar, and an older man singing as he accompanies himself on the lyre. The Berlin Painter appreciated better than anyone else how the dramatic contrast between a matt red figure and the glossy black background was boldest at its most simple — one on one. The spot-lit effect gives his figures a statuesque presence rarely rivalled at this scale. The multi-figure scenes of his contemporaries often look fussy by comparison.

Nearly 300 vases by the Berlin Painter are known, most, like this one, from burials in Italy, the destination of much Athenian pottery exported at this time. The artist's career covers roughly the first third of the fifth century, down to about 460 BC. This is the period of transition between the Archaic and Classical Styles, the time when Greek sculptors were executing the first fully naturalistic representations of the human body in bronze and marble. In vase painting, too, attention was shifting from purely decorative effects and the rendering of particular anatomical details (eyes, knees and so on) to more challenging problems concerning pose and composition, the ability to show the body in movement or in awkward positions. Although the Berlin Painter was less innovative in this area than some of his colleagues — he shied away from three-quarter views of limbs or faces — he took on board the major advances of the age and applied them as well as anyone. He gets the youth's twisting torso — the only real challenge in this piece — almost right. Rendering the stomach muscles and ribs in fluid lines

of thinned paint, he has managed to convey the essential form and quality of the anatomy more effectively than the previous generation (cat. no. 64). Men's unnaturally heavy thighs have thinned down further. Drapery, on the other hand, is still rather starched (especially the folds over the youth's right arm). Faces are stereotypes: the handsome youth, indistinguishable from hundreds of others, and the middle-aged singer, his maturity marked by the formulaic balding hairline and beard. The only added colour now is some purple on the wreaths; fifth-century artists wisely eschewed this gilding of the lily. The Berlin Painter has a particular penchant for animals, and here gives a sympathetic treatment to the Maltese dog accompanying the older man.

The Berlin Painter was an exquisite draughtsman, combining impeccable technique with an unrivalled elegance of line. The drawing is clear and confident, the internal detailing of muscles and drapery restrained and accurate, giving his figures a rare gracefulness and charm. Simple scenes from everyday life, especially single figure studies, suit his purism better than dramatic mythological subjects, which he avoided. The contemplative mood of the studied, isolated figure invites the viewer to share in the artist's passion for the perfect line.

The Berlin Painter's name is not known, unless he was the Gorgos who is named as the potter on an early piece attributed on stylistic grounds to his hand: many potters were also painters, though there is no proof in this case.

This vase belongs to the middle period of the Berlin Painter's career, before his hand began to falter and his output became dull and repetitive. It was probably painted within a decade of the great Persian invasion of 480 BC.

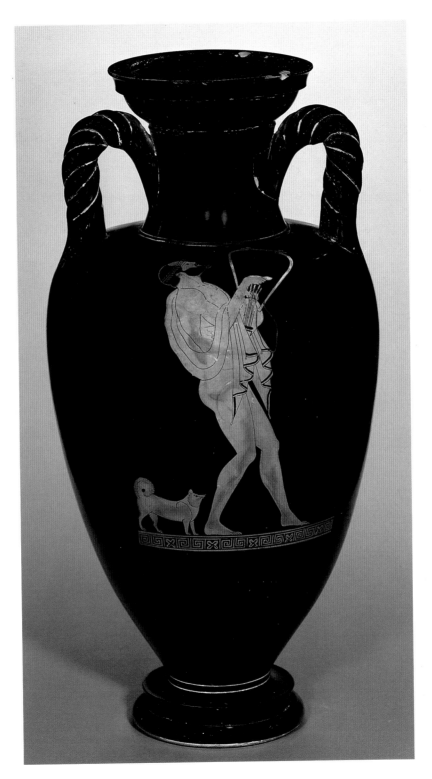

Hermes, messenger of the gods

Italian adaptation of a Greek statue
of c.400–200 BC
c.50 BC (Republican Period)
Saponara, southern Italy
bronze
49.0 cm height
cat. no. 67

One image above all others has come to epitomize the essence of Classical art — the standing male nude. The well-muscled Greek athlete or god has proved one of the most compelling and memorable images in the history of art — and one that, since the return to Classical models in the Renaissance, has had a continuing impact on the Western artistic tradition. Unlike the mummies which hold a similar place in our picture-book conception of Egypt, this is not a purely modern obsession. Greco-Roman thought was thoroughly humanistic, and the tendency to perceive and analyze the world in human terms infused Classical art with an abiding preoccupation with the human form.

The broad traveller's hat on this statuette marks it as Hermes (Roman Mercury), the fleet-footed messenger of the gods and 'guider of souls' into the underworld. His right hand originally held a herald's wand or money pouch, but he lacks the winged sandals that are the god's other usual attribute.

As befits the patron deity of young men and gymnastic sports, Hermes is shown as a well-muscled figure in the prime of early manhood. He stands relaxed, the weight of his body supported on one braced leg while the other trails behind. This causes the hip-line to dip towards the side of the limp leg, which must then be balanced by an opposite slant in the shoulders. Individually these changes from the regimented pose of the Archaic *kouros* (cat. no. 65) were minor, but together they constituted a revolution which marked nothing less than the dawn of the Classical Period in Greek sculpture. The accurate proportions of body parts and muscle contours which had been the final achievement of the Archaic Period were now given a plausible structure in figures which stood or moved in life-like poses, with the body weight shifted casually onto one leg and a realistic balancing of tensed and limp limbs. In the decades after 500 BC, for the first time in the history of art, the male body began to be understood as a complex structure of moving parts, a structure capable of infinite variation — though always subject to a natural logic of stresses and balances.

The classic statement of this new understanding was the *Spear Carrier* of about 440 BC, carved by Polyclitus as an illustration of his new system of bodily proportions, but demonstrating also the novel appreciation of the shifting bodyweight in a natural stance and how this effects other parts of the figure. The same fundamental formula of one braced and one trailing leg, with hips and shoulders sloping in opposite directions, was used time and again throughout the Classical Period as the basis for sculptures of gods and athletes in repose. Heads may turn in different directions, arms are adjusted to hold the appropriate attributes, but the legs and torso remain essentially unchanged in countless works down to Roman times.

The well-conceived and flawlessly modelled figure of this Hermes has more the air of a lost masterpiece than a copyist's anachronistic 'creation', but which particular sculpture may have formed its model is now impossible to say. Although a number of fifth-century BC sculptors are known to have made statues of Hermes, matching the names to surviving works (themselves almost all copies) is now largely guesswork. The figure's limp right arm and trailing leg, his sharp, clear muscles, and the exaggerated swelling on the hip where the torso muscles meet the groin line are still very close to the *Spear Carrier* of Polyclitus, one of the sculptors who made a lost statue of the god; but there are also features which would be more at home in the fourth century BC or later — the placement of the left hand casually on the hip; the small round head; and the bulbous, rather contracted chest muscles which replace the broad planes in works such as the *Spear Carrier*.

It is appropriate that this Hermes survives in bronze, which was the preferred medium of Classical sculptors. Building up a figure in clay (to be then cast in bronze) was a more forgiving process to the would-be naturalist than carving away at a stone block, where mistakes could not be undone. And the final layer of wax applied to the surface of the clay before encasing it in a mould gave much greater scope for rendering fine detail, as in the hands, feet and face in this work. The rare surviving bronze originals of the Classical Period show how inferior a guide to the masterpieces of the age marble copies can be.

This statuette was found in southern Italy where it was probably made in about the first century BC. The Romans were by then in firm control of *Magna Graecia* (Greater Greece), as the region came to be called, but the Greek population retained many cultural links with their homeland and Rome was itself falling increasingly under the Greek artistic spell.

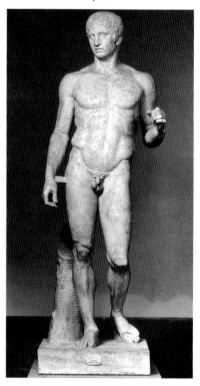

The *Spear Carrier* by Polyclitus, c.440 BC, a Roman copy from the Naples Museum. (Hirmer Archive)

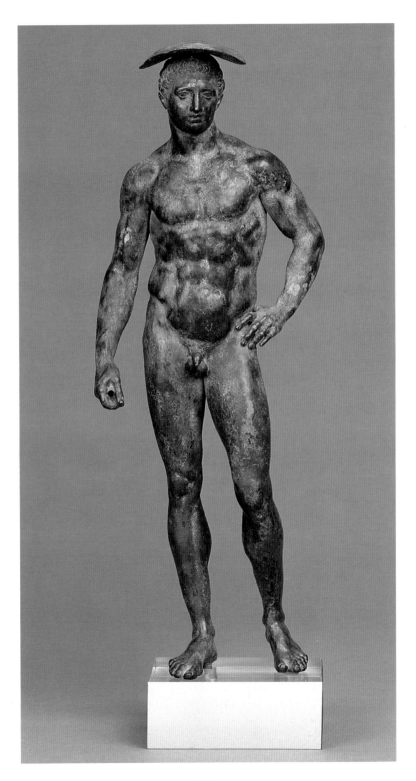

cat. no. 67

139

Young man with a horse and dog

**Roman relief in the Classical Greek Style
of c.450 BC**

c.AD 120 (Imperial Period)
from Hadrian's villa, Tivoli, near Rome, Italy
marble
75.0 x 101.8 cm
cat. no. **68**

'Conquered Greece took her rude captor captive and brought the arts to rustic Latium (Italy)'. Thus the Roman poet Horace described the mania for Greek culture that gripped Rome in the last two centuries before Christ, as the great new power of the ancient world extended her rule over the city-states of the Aegean and eventually throughout the entire eastern Mediterranean.

Nowhere is the Greek impact on Rome more apparent than in the visual arts. From the second century BC, when Roman troops marched into the cities of Greece, her sculptures and other movable *objets d'art* were systematically pillaged and shipped back to Italy. Such was the demand for things Greek that workshops were soon established which specialized in copying famous works and creating new pieces in Greek styles. Greek fashion became the touchstone of sophistication, the mark of the civilized man. Puritanical Romans regarded such mannerisms as unmanly and socially disruptive, a threat to the traditional Republican virtues of austerity and strength on which Rome's greatness was founded. But they represented the voice of the past. Roman arts and culture were already greatly indebted to Greece, whose traditions increasingly provided the inspiration for fashions among the upper classes and later even for the imperial family itself.

One of the greatest of all admirers of Greek culture was the emperor Hadrian (AD 117–138). He grew a beard in the Greek manner and stocked his villa at Tivoli outside Rome with fine copies of all the best Greek works, thus bequeathing a veritable treasure trove of Classical sculpture to the modern world. It was here, in a lake known as the Pantanello, that the present relief was found in 1770 by the Scottish antiquities dealer Gavin Hamilton. The English collector Charles Townley bought it through the Italian artist and antiquarian Piranesi for £40.

It belongs to the class of pseudo-Greek reliefs carved in the days of the late Roman Republic and early Empire (first century BC to second century AD), and called Neo-Attic because the sculptors sometimes signed themselves as Athenians (Athens being the capital of Attica). Many are accurate copies of Greek originals, but others are free modifications or even completely new creations in the manner of older styles. There are no other known examples of this particular depiction of the subject, which may therefore be a Roman adaptation of Hadrian's day.

We see a young man, naked but for the cape tied at his neck, restraining a rearing horse by its bridle (this was added in bronze and has not survived, but the attachment holes are visible). The hound bringing up the rear suggests that they are on a hunt, the sort of aristocratic pastime which particularly appealed to Hadrian. In this work, however, the dog adds nothing to the composition (indeed it would be better balanced without it) and is probably the sculptor's addition to a simpler Greek scene; the all-too-perfect fit of its head into the curve of the horse's hind leg introduces an annoying element into an otherwise very successful composition.

As is typical of Neo-Attic reliefs, the sculptor has imitated the outward forms of an earlier style — here the mid-fifth century BC — but adapted it in ways which betray the different aesthetics and purposes of his own day. The balanced composition and flowing forms; the man's serene, passionless face (there is more expression in the dog's pricked ears and horse's open mouth!); the loose radiating locks of hair tied with a head-band; the neatly fluttering cape; and the restrained naturalism of the smoothly modelled musculature — all these are distinctive marks of the early Classical Style.

But the figures have an exaggerated elegance bordering on mannerism which is alien to original works of that period. This reflects the Neo-Attic sculptor's essentially decorative aims. Such reliefs were carved first and foremost as attractive backdrops for the refined 'good life' of the wealthy Roman. Stylistic fidelity was often sacrificed in the cause of greater decorative appeal, even to the point of combining elements from different sources and periods. The narrow-waisted man and his fine-ankled animals are slimmed down from the Classical canon almost to the point of effeteness. A man restraining his horse in almost exactly the same way on the Parthenon frieze (so close indeed that our work may have been directly inspired by it) provides a telling comparison. The Parthenon horse has much heavier, more realistic proportions; and the man has none of the daintiness of our figure, who manages to restrain his rearing steed — a quite vigorous act — with the grace and poise of a ballet-dancer.

Parts of the relief were restored in the eighteenth century; the in-set pieces of marble are clearly visible.

Man restraining horse, from the west frieze of the Parthenon, Athens, c.440 BC. Cast, Ashmolean Museum, Oxford. (R.L. Wilkins, courtesy Prof. Sir John Boardman)

cat. no. **68**

Head of Heracles

Roman copy from a Greek statue of c.470 BC
c.AD 120 (Imperial Period)
from Hadrian's villa, Tivoli, near Rome, Italy
marble
72.0 cm height
cat. no. 69

The colossal scale and heroic face of this head can indicate none other than Heracles (Roman Hercules), the great strong-man of Greco-Roman legend. Technical features of the carving, especially the use of the drill for the heavily undercut ringlets of hair, mark it clearly as a Roman creation of the time of Hadrian (AD 117–138), in whose villa it was found. But like many of the Roman emperor's sculptures, the style is not entirely of his era. The heroic bearded head with its sharply defined features and large eyes was conceived in the Severe Style of Classical Greek art that flourished over five centuries earlier. The full figure, which survives in another Roman copy (the *Cherchel Heracles*), shows the hero standing relaxed, resting his club on the ground and holding what is probably a bow in the other hand. The original, probably a colossal bronze of about 470 BC, must have been the work of a leading sculptor, but attributing it to a particular artist — Myron and Onatas have been suggested — is now little more than guesswork.

The Romans had a taste for grandiose scale which the larger-than-life hero of Greek legend provided a perfect opportunity to indulge. The eight-month-old baby who strangled two giant serpents in his cot grew into a massive muscle-bound figure some seven feet (over two metres) high.

This head shows Heracles in middle age, the trials and tribulations of his many arduous exploits reflected in the low, heavy brow. The beard, a mark of maturity in Greek art, here serves also to emphasize his role as the archetype of male strength and virility.

These qualities made Heracles the universal Greek (and later Roman) hero, the mighty sportsman and warrior who fought tirelessly for honour, glory and the welfare of mankind, prevailing against overwhelming odds and all manner of fearsome creatures armed only with his enormous club and bow.

The most famous of his deeds were the twelve 'labours' undertaken for his evil cousin, the King of Argolis. These included killing with his bare hands the Nemean lion (whose skin provided the cape which became his constant signature), cutting off the multiple serpent heads of the monstrous Hydra, and cleaning out the Augean stables.

This and more he achieved where all lesser mortals would have failed. As the son of Zeus by a Greek queen, he already had a touch of the divine, and in some myths the final reward for his many noble deeds was nothing less than immortality. But even this apotheosis, as the Greeks called it, did not come easily. His estranged wife was tricked into thinking she could regain his affections by making him wear what proved to be a poisoned coat. His skin burned and torn by the magic garment, Heracles built himself a funeral pyre and prepared to end his agony. The gods, however, would not see him perish and as the flames consumed him, thunder roared and the noblest of mortals was lifted to the heavens on a cloud. There he was married to Hebe, the goddess of youth.

The British Museum Heracles was discovered by the antiquities dealer Gavin Hamilton in 1769 in the Pantanello at Hadrian's villa at Tivoli, the artificial lake which also yielded cat. nos 68 and 86. The head later passed to the artist and antiquarian Piranesi, who sold it to the collector Charles Townley in 1772 for less than £9.

The chest and stand, as well as the tip of the nose, the right eyelid and the edges of the ears, have been restored.

Statuette of Heracles, probably a copy of a fifth-century BC statue by Myron.
(Ashmolean Museum, Oxford)

cat. no. 69

Herm-portrait of Pericles

Roman copy of a Greek bronze portrait by
Kresilas made soon after 429 BC
c.AD 50–150 (Imperial Period)
from the 'Villa of Cassius', Tivoli, near Rome, Italy
marble
59.0 cm height
cat. no. **70**

This portrait head is based on a contemporary image of Pericles, that most famous of all Greek statesmen who dominated political and cultural life during Athens's 'golden age'. Born into a prominent Athenian family around 500 BC, it was Pericles who put the finishing touches to the newly-born democracy, the novel form of government which, as he later said, made Athens 'the school of Greece'. In his day this claim was arguable (Greek philosophers were largely hostile to democracy), but in more recent times his vision of active popular government has proved an inspiration to generations of political theorists and reformers. Under his direction, the Athenian navy became undisputed mistress of the seas, and when Athens became embroiled in war with her old rival Sparta it was Pericles who, through the force of his personality, directed strategy until his untimely death of plague in 429 BC.

Today it is Pericles' more tangible achievements as a builder that we are best able to appreciate. For it was he who inspired the rebuilding of the Athenian Acropolis, with the Parthenon as its centrepiece, adorned with the magnificent sculptures (mostly now in the British Museum) that have come to epitomize the spirit of the Classical Age.

The portrait of Pericles is a Roman copy of a fifth-century BC original, probably the bronze statue by the sculptor Kresilas, erected in Athens to commemorate the great statesman soon after his death in 429 BC. Although this would make it a near-contemporary representation, it was not a true portrait in the modern sense, but a highly idealized image, conditioned as much by how such a person was supposed to look — strong, dignified, statesmanlike — as by his actual features. It remains largely an amalgamation of symbols: the beard symbolizes Pericles' maturity; the clear, firm features his commanding character; and the helmet his generalship — the whole imbued with that peculiarly Classical quality of aloof detachment which led the ancients to call him 'Olympian'. The result is a portrait which conveys not so much a personality as a role. And in an age when art aimed above all to be edifying, this is probably how Kresilas would have liked it. Admiring the statue of Pericles, the Roman writer Pliny remarked: 'It is a marvellous thing how in this art noble men are made to appear still nobler'.

Realistic portraiture as we know it was a relatively late development. To begin with, it presupposes an interest in anatomical detail and a technical ability for naturalistic carving that was not attained in Greek art until the fifth century BC. And even then, the temptation to pursue truly thorough-going realism was largely held in check by the idealizing imperative of Classical art, which required that man be portrayed in his most noble and perfect form. Public portraits were a great honour reserved for those who had rendered outstanding service to the state, and they had to be sufficiently idealized to convey the brilliance which alone merited commemoration. Relatively few attempts were made to capture accurately a man's physical features before the Hellenistic Period, when kings, influenced by Near Eastern styles of rule, began to have their images widely and conspicuously displayed.

Pericles is shown with his helmet pushed back over his head. This is not inappropriate for the man who was elected general for the last fifteen years of his life, but the immediate reason for the device, as Plutarch tells us, was to hide Pericles' unusually long, bulbous head.

Kresilas' original statue would have shown Pericles full-length, probably standing nude and armed; but no details are known since the existing copies show only the head and neck set at the top of a square pillar (*herm*). Greek *herms* were sacred images originally with gods' heads and a phallus on the pillar, but the Romans used the form more widely as a way of adapting any full-length Greek portrait to their native tradition of bust-sculpture.

The nose, and parts of the helmet, are modern restorations.

cat. no. 70

Greek gravestone of Xanthippos

c.430 BC (Classical Period)
Athens, Greece
marble
83.3 cm height
cat. no. 71

The modern world first came to know Classical Greek sculpture through Roman copies. The Renaissance was fuelled by discoveries made on Italian soil and this remained the main source of archaeological finds for many years after. Though he did not know it, Charles Townley, the great English collector of the late eighteenth century, bought only one Classical Greek sculpture — this Athenian gravestone — the rest being all Hellenistic works and Roman copies. Even during his lifetime, however, things were changing: excavation in Greece was beginning to take off and, as more original material emerged from the homeland of the Classical Style, the differences between Greek and Roman art began to be appreciated. Led by the great German scholar Johann Winckelmann, early critics tended to deride Roman art as derivative and second-rate. Although this was an extreme reaction, there is no denying the advantage of studying Greek art in the original, as far as it is available. This gravestone is therefore an important foil to the Roman copies which inevitably dominate the selection of 'Greek' sculpture displayed here (cat. nos 68–70, 82, 83, 86, 87), as indeed they still dominate most modern collections of Classical art outside Greece.

The gravestone was carved in Athens to mark the burial of an otherwise unknown Xanthippos, whose name is inscribed along the top. By trade he may have been a cobbler — that is, if the foot he holds up is correctly interpreted as a last for shaping shoes. A lowly craftsman could hardly have afforded such a fine tomb relief, however, and one might suspect that it was commissioned by a grateful master for his favourite slave. With Xanthippos are shown his two daughters, represented — as was the convention of the day — with the proportions and faces of miniature adults. The elder child holds what seems to be a bird. The gesture of the younger girl, reaching for the model foot, is less clear. Perhaps she is just expressing every child's incorrigible interest in whatever the nearest adult is holding. If this were a cartoon one could imagine her saying: 'Daddy, give me!'.

Xanthippos' gravestone is one of the earliest of the series which revived this form of commemoration in Athens in about 430 BC after a fifty-year gap. This was the time of the plague which afflicted the Athenians in the early years of the Peloponnesian War, leaving thousands of men, women and children dead, including their foremost statesman Pericles. Most were buried in mass graves just outside the city. It was also the time when Pericles' massive building program on the Acropolis — with the Parthenon as the jewel in the crown — was winding down. This freed scores of stone-masons and sculptors to work on private commissions.

The sculptor of Xanthippos' gravestone was probably one of these exceptional artists who brought to their work not only the skills and experience they had acquired, but sometimes also echoes of the subjects they had portrayed in Pericles' great works. Although only a humble craftsman, Xanthippos sits like one of the Olympians: heroically nude from the waist up, striking a noble profile worthy of Zeus himself as he protectively shepherds his young daughter. Of his facial features, we are given precious little indication in the stereotyped heroic profile (compare cat. no. 70) which the sculptor carves. His beard manifests maturity, but wrinkles are banished, and the only indications of age in his strong, well-built body are the slightly hunched posture and a certain flabbiness about the chest. Under the chisel of the Classical sculptor, even a humble cobbler could live on in the image of the gods.

The dead were often shown on these gravestones in the company of those they had left behind, either bidding them farewell or in scenes recalling happy times together.

The collector Charles Townley purchased this stela from the estate of another collector in 1778 for £20.

cat. no. 71

Engraved Greek gems

Minoan Greek seal-stone showing a man
leading a bull by the horns; probably strung on
a bracelet or necklace
c.1450–1200 BC, Late Bronze Age
(Minoan Period)
Crete, Greece
agate (lentil-shaped)
2.2 x 2.3 cm

cat. no. 72

Greek gem showing a lion attacking a stag;
perhaps carved by Dexamenos; probably worn
as a pendant
c.450–425 BC (Classical Period)
findspot unknown
rock crystal (scarab-shaped)
2.0 x 1.5 cm

cat. no. 73

Greek gem showing Nike (Victory) erecting
a trophy; probably worn as a pendant
c.400–350 BC (Classical Period)
findspot unknown
blue chalcedony (scarab-shaped)
3.3 x 2.7 cm

cat. no. 74

Pergamene Greek ring-stone showing
Philetaerus, ruler of Pergamum (western Turkey)
282–263 BC
c.275–250 BC (Hellenistic Period)
findspot unknown
chalcedony with yellow jasper inclusions (ovoid)
2.8 x 2.3 cm

cat. no. 75

Engraved gems rank among the finest artistic and technical masterpieces of the Classical world. With extraordinary skill, the ancient engravers of Greece and Rome were able to render minute figures less than a centimetre high with a degree of detail and finesse that seems almost to defy nature. Musculature, drapery and even the facial features of their diminutive figures are carved with such remarkable dexterity that photographic enlargements many times actual size have hardly any effect on the sense of detail and finish. This is all the more astonishing when one remembers that they were carved in intaglio, that is by cutting into the flat surface of the stone to create a negative form like a mould. This reflects their original purpose as seals: the positive relief image was created when the gem was impressed into soft clay or wax.

To the Greeks this was no minor art. The master gem-engravers were on an equal footing with the finest goldsmiths, painters and sculptors of the day. Alexander the Great entrusted the carving of his gem portraits solely to Pyrgoteles, the pre-eminent engraver of his generation, just as he allowed only Lysippus to carve his portrait in sculpture and only Apelles to depict his image in paint. This was a pointer to the future; in the Hellenistic and Roman Periods almost all the finest gem engravers were attached to the royal courts and imperial households.

The harder, more exotic gem stones and the technology for carving them were introduced into Greece from the Near East, first in the Bronze Age and again in the sixth century BC. But each time the Greeks improved upon the achievements of their Oriental mentors, displaying a talent for naturalistic carving and a sense of movement that were rarely rivalled in the East. Something of these qualities, the hallmark of Bronze Age Cretan art, is illustrated in cat. no. 72, whose sympathetic rendering of the bull is a skilful piece of elegant naturalism. Such seals are among the finest works of any medium in Bronze Age art.

A greater degree of naturalism was not achieved until the Classical Period, represented here by cat. nos 73 and 74. By this time, all vestiges of the decoration apparent in the Archaic Style had been sacrificed in the quest for ever more life-like effects. The result, remarkable enough in full-scale sculpture and painting, is all the more astonishing an achievement at this eye-straining scale. Even with modern tools these gems would be considered technical masterpieces. The tensed muscles, the veins and claws of the lion in cat. no. 73; the open-mouthed, wide-eyed terror of its stumbling victim; the voluptuous curves of Nike's arched torso in cat. no. 74; her perfectly defined face and feet; the flowing drapery and wing-feathers — all these are rendered in minute yet utterly convincing detail. Both gems are clearly the work of master engravers whose skills bear comparison with the best of any age. Nike's engraver gives what are probably two letters

of his name, 'ND' (previously misread as part of 'Onatas'), on the pennant fluttering from the spear.

The development of portrait sculpture in the Hellenistic Period (see cat. nos 85, 86) soon found its way onto gems. The finest portrait gems are royal likenesses cut by artists attached to the Hellenistic courts. These have clear affiliations with the heads on coins (compare cat. no. 79), and the dies used to strike coins — a jealously guarded royal prerogative — may often have been engraved by the same artists.

The portrait gem here (cat. no. 75) is of Philetaerus, the colourful if duplicitous eunuch who ruled Pergamum in western Turkey from 282 to 263 BC. According to the ancient writer Strabo, his unfortunate start in life occurred at a funeral display when 'the nurse who was carrying Philetaerus, still an infant, was caught in the crowd and pressed so hard that the child was incapacitated'. Whatever the circumstances — this story may be a smoke-screen to disguise his servile origins — Philetaerus grew up emasculated, a condition which shows in his heavy jowls. He proved, nonetheless, a shrewd and wily operator in the treacherous world of Hellenistic politics. When the moment was right, he betrayed Lysimachus, the ruler of Thrace, whose rich treasury at Pergamum he had been assigned to guard, in favour of Lysimachus' arch-enemy Seleucus. The great wealth that thereby fell to Philetaerus provided him with a power-base which his successors consolidated into one of the richest and most glorious kingdoms of the Hellenistic world, boasting a lavish court life and library second only to that of Alexandria in Egypt.

The portrait shows Philetaerus without the royal wreath which he wears on the coins produced by his Pergamene successors. This has been taken to indicate that it was carved during his lifetime, when he still paid nominal obeisance to the King of Syria. Such fine carving might well have been executed for Philetaerus himself, either to be given to a high official or for his own finger-ring.

  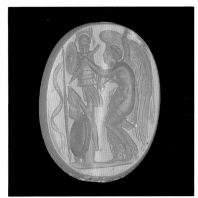 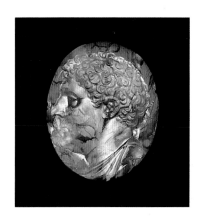

cat. no. **72**   cat. no. **73**   cat. no. **74**   cat. no. **75**

Coins from Lydia and the Greek world

Stater of King Croesus of Lydia showing the confronting foreparts of a lion and a bull (obverse) and two incuse squares (reverse)
c.560–520 BC (Archaic Period)
minted in Sardis, Lydia (western Turkey)
gold
1.6 cm length; 8.04 g weight
cat. no. 76

Two Athenian tetradrachms showing the head of Athena (obverse) and an owl and olive sprig (reverse); inscribed ATHE (abbreviation for ATHENAION, 'of the Athenians')
c.510 BC (Archaic Period)
minted in Athens, Greece
silver
2.5 cm, 2.6 cm diameters; 17.19 g, 17.23 g weights
cat. no. 77

Tetradrachm showing a squatting Silenus with a wine-cup (obverse) and a profile head of Dionysus (reverse); inscribed NAXION ('of the Naxians')
c.460 BC (Classical Period)
minted in Naxus, Sicily
silver
2.7 cm diameter; 17.44 g weight
cat. no. 78

Tetradrachm of Lysimachus, King of Thrace, showing head of Alexander the Great with ram's horn of Zeus-Ammon (obverse) and seated Athena holding winged figure of Nike (Victory) who crowns the name of Lysimachus (reverse); inscribed BASILEOS LYSIMACHOU ('of King Lysimachus') and issue-mark of Pergamum, N, (reverse) and issue mark, K, (obverse)
287–282 BC (Hellenistic Period)
minted by Lysimachus in Pergamum (western Turkey)
silver
3.0 cm diameter; 17.22 g weight
cat. no. 79

Although metals had long been used as a medium of exchange in the Near East, the first true coins — lumps of metal of standard sizes with a stamped design or 'type' — were not produced until the seventh century BC. According to the Greek historian Herodotus, the people who invented the technique were the Lydians of western Turkey, who made their coins from rich local deposits of electrum, a natural alloy of gold and silver. The last and most famous of their kings was Croesus (reigned 560–546 BC), and the first pure gold and pure silver coinages, bearing the confronting foreparts of a lion and a bull (cat. no. 76), were until recently all attributed to him. He may indeed have begun these series, but many of the bull-and-lion coins seem to have been produced after 546 BC, when Lydia fell to the Persians. Sardis, the Lydian capital, continued to function as a major mint for the Persian Empire. This coin is from the earlier series probably issued by Croesus.

Croesus' fabulous wealth was legendary among the Greeks, and memory of it still survives today in our expression 'as rich as Croesus'. Herodotus relates how Croesus once asked the Athenian sage Solon who was the happiest man in the world, expecting Solon to name Croesus himself, the richest of all men. But Solon did not, explaining that no man could be called truly happy while he lived, for any fate might still befall him — a lesson which Croesus soon had cause to recall as he saw his kingdom fall prey to the Persians.

Some decades later, probably during the rule of the tyrant Hippias (527–510 BC), Athens, too, produced a standardized state coinage, replacing the numerous different emblems which had been circulating earlier in the sixth century BC. Naturally enough, the Athenians chose for the designs of their new currency the head of their state deity Athena on one side, and her sacred animal the owl on the other (cat. no. 77). While many other cities regularly changed their coin designs, these types, with only minor modifications, were to remain the unmistakable symbols of Athenian currency for almost three centuries. The examples shown here were struck in about 510 BC.

The goddess is shown in her military aspect wearing a helmet. Her profile face, curiously archaic in style, would have looked old-fashioned even when these coins were first produced. Frontal faces were used on Greek coins chiefly for dramatic effect or to emphasize ugliness, but the engraver could not resist the temptation to show Athena's bird in its typically inquisitive attitude, glaring fixedly forward.

By the late sixth century BC coinage was being widely minted throughout the Greek world. Many of the finest designs were engraved by artists in the Greek cities of southern Italy and Sicily. The coin issued by Naxus in Sicily (cat. no. 78) around 460 BC bears one of the most originally conceived and skilfully executed of all Classical types — a remarkable squatting Silenus holding a wine cup. Like his close relatives the satyrs, the wine-god Dionysus' older companion has a human body, a snub-nosed, bestial face and horse's tail and ears. The musculature of his frontal torso is rendered with great accuracy and subtlety; but it is in the masterly foreshortening of his unabashedly parted legs — one projecting squarely forward, the other obliquely to one side, with the feet drawn in to the buttocks — that the engraver displays the full extent of his skill. The result has justly been called 'one of the assured masterpieces of Greek art of this time'. And it is indeed a *tour de force* of early Classical naturalism, demonstrating an almost flawless mastery of the male nude in miniature. The other side of the coin bears a bold but conventional profile head of the wine-god himself.

The occasion of this coin issue was probably the return of the inhabitants of Naxus from exile in the nearby town of Leontini (whence they had been banished by Hieron, the tyrant of Syracuse) around 461 BC.

The Greeks of the Classical Period were reluctant to place portraits of their leaders on coins, an ostentation they associated with the Persians and despotism. Even Alexander the Great refrained from so overt an assumption of absolute power, allowing only that the features of Heracles — a traditional Macedonian coin type — be modified slightly to resemble his own. But after Alexander's death, his generals, eager to outdo each other in expressions of homage and thereby associate themselves more closely with his legacy, proved less inhibited. For some years they continued to issue coins with Alexander's types, modelling Heracles' face more closely on their dead king. Later, some of them went a stage further and issued coins with unambiguous portraits of Alexander, often bearing attributes alluding to his conquests and divine powers: the scalp of an elephant for the conqueror of India; Zeus' goatskin cape (*aegis*) and a ram's horn for the son of Zeus-Ammon. Although idealized, they are recognizable as images of Alexander, the basic profile probably deriving from miniature portraits by his gem-cutter Pyrgoteles.

Cat. no. 79 was issued by Lysimachus (323–281 BC), one of Alexander's most trusted generals and bodyguards. Upon the king's death, Lysimachus took control of Thrace (north-eastern Greece), later extending his control over much of northern Greece and Turkey. In 297 BC he began issuing coins with portraits of Alexander. They show the young conqueror wearing the headband of kingship and the ram's horn which signified his identification as the son of the Greco-Egyptian god Zeus-Ammon (Amun-Re), a strange association which was the result of a pilgrimage Alexander undertook to Ammon's distant oasis sanctuary at Siwah in the Egyptian desert.

Although Alexander's public image was strictly controlled by selected court artists, near-contemporary portraits like this, the best preserved example of Lysimachus' currency, may be accepted as reasonable likenesses. The artistic licence which gives the king a prominent, care-worn brow and large, deep-set eyes is in the nature of exaggeration rather than invention, a typically Greek attempt to convey the personal qualities which made him a worthy object of portraiture. Alexander was the greatest military leader the world had known, and his portraits had to show it. The sculptures of Lysippus had represented him with deep-set, upward-glancing eyes, tousled mane-like hair and slightly parted lips. These features, particularly the eyes, were further exaggerated in the coin portraits, lending his strong, handsome face a hint of pathos and fatalism. There is a sense of tragic destiny in the distant, melting gaze of this idealistic conqueror who, at thirty-two, died too young to impose his vision on the world he had already done so much to change.

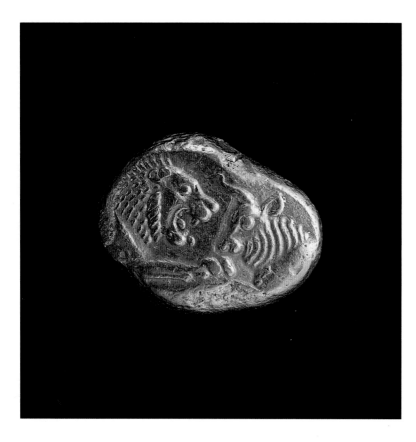

cat. no. 76   cat. no. 77

cat. no. 78

cat. no. 79

Athenian jar by the Marsyas Painter

Peleus pursuing the sea-nymph Thetis
*c.*350 BC (Classical Period)
Camirus, Rhodes, Greece; made in Athens,
Greece
painted pottery ('Kerch Style')
42.5 cm height
cat. no. 80

The crouching white figure in the centre of this vase is the nymph Thetis, most beautiful of the fifty daughters of the sea-god Nereus. She is grasped by her suitor Peleus, a legendary king of Phthia, in northern Greece. Zeus himself had lusted after Thetis but shied away when an oracle foretold that her son would be stronger than his father. The gods prudently decided that she should marry a mortal and Peleus was chosen. But Thetis had other ideas and fiercely resisted Peleus' advances, changing herself into all manner of monstrous beasts and elements of nature to escape his hold. In a late version of the myth she turns first into fire, then to water, wind, a tree, a bird, a tiger, a lion, a snake and finally into a cuttle-fish, but Peleus holds on through every metamorphosis. At last she relents and changes back into the beautiful nymph that she is. The couple were duly married before the gods, and Thetis bore Peleus seven children. In a mad attempt to make them immortal, Thetis cast the first six into burning flames, but Peleus rescued the last-born just in time. Thus was saved Achilles, the future hero of the Trojan War.

Thetis is shown changing to or from human form, her arm held firmly by the determined Peleus, and also in the form of a sea-monster biting Peleus' leg. Around the grappling couple the love-goddess Aphrodite looks on from above (seated top left) while winged Eros, the harbinger of passion, hovers overhead. Next to Thetis, her distressed companion prepares to flee, and the two other nude Nereids (daughters of Nereus) seem likewise to have given up on their sister, one of them pirouetting on her heel as she turns to leave.

Splashes of colour and gilding — white for flesh; blue, green and gold for wings, garments, and head-dresses — do much to enhance the painting's decorative effect.

Thetis' white flesh here serves also to single her out from the other nude Nereids as the dramatic focus of the scene. The revival of this Archaic device (see cat. no. 63) was probably inspired by the curious practice in contemporary wall-painting of using highlights and shading only for male skin and naturally shiny objects like metal, while women were still rendered in a single undifferentiated tone. On the whole, however, red-figure vase-painting of the fourth century BC is an increasingly unreliable guide to the advances in realistic effects being made by the great wall-painters of the day. Their paintings depended more and more on gradations of colour and tone which pot-painters could hardly begin to convey in what was essentially a linear style.

Added colour first began to be used liberally on Athenian pottery around 400 BC. Having by then mastered all the essentially draughting challenges of twisting, turning figures and foreshortened limbs, vase-painters were being forced to look elsewhere for new visual effects, and colour was a natural avenue to explore. To artists of the Berlin Painter's generation (cat. no. 66), who rarely interrupted the simple formula of red-on-black, the colourists' flourishes would have seemed like gilding the lily, and there is no denying that the rich polychrome pieces of the early fourth century BC can indeed be garish. But in mid-century vases like this, where a degree of restraint has returned, the result is a considerable decorative success. This type of work, which lasted from about 370 to 340 BC, is known as the 'Kerch Style', after the site in southern Russia where much of it has been found.

Colour in vase-painting was only one aspect of a more general fashion for decorative effects, which is a hallmark of fourth-century Greek art. The trend has been thought to reflect the belated assertion of feminine taste, and it is certainly true that female deities, love scenes and other 'unmasculine' subjects become more common at this time, especially on mirrors, perfume bottles and other feminine articles (see cat. no. 81). The aesthetic which conditioned works like this vase was pro-

foundly different from the Berlin Painter's austere elegance (cat. no. 66). Clear composition in bold red and black has given way to a crowded scene, full of mannered gestures, swirling drapery and bright colour. The effect is pretty rather than beautiful; decorative rather than moving — symptoms perhaps of an art which no longer reflects developments in the major arts.

Sculptors and painters also faced an impasse as their mastery of the human form improved. Sculptors of the fourth century BC found new challenges in rendering age, character and emotion — themes that stimulated and enlivened Greek sculpture for many years to come. But for figured vase-painting the fourth century BC was in many ways the end of the road, and plain black-glazed pots, often with moulded designs, tended thereafter to predominate. Provincial schools producing figured decoration survived in southern Italy, but they rarely attained the standards of previous generations.

The reverse of the vase shows Dionysus between a satyr and maenad.

Greek engraved mirror cover

Aphrodite playing knuckle-bones with Pan
c.350 BC (Classical Period)
Greece (Corinth ?)
bronze
18.5 cm diameter
cat. no. 81

This mirror cover of the late Classical Period shows the Greek love-goddess Aphrodite playing knuckle-bones with Pan, the half-man, half-goat shepherd-god. Behind Aphrodite, the child-like figure of the winged love-god Eros, her regular companion (and in some ancient stories her offspring), watches attentively — in marked contrast to the goose under the table, which strikes a pose eloquent of total disinterest.

The relaxed attitudes of the figures evoke well the casual atmosphere appropriate to a scene of the gods at play: Aphrodite sits on the edge of the table, supporting the weight of her ample torso on one arm as she throws the gaming pieces with the other; Eros, leaning forward on the goddess's thigh, gestures with his free arm at the result of the throw; and Pan — a truly brilliant image — squats on the table-top, his hands emphatically making the point to which his slightly parted lips are about to give voice. Is he claiming victory, or warning his contestant? He had good reason to despair of defeating her at a game in which the winning throw was known as an 'Aphrodite'.

The high quality of draughtsmanship on this and similar mirrors brings us close to the lost masterpieces of Classical wall-painting, some of which may indeed have been copied by mirror engravers. There was a flourishing school of wall-painting in the fourth century BC at Sicyon near Corinth, where this piece is reported to have been found.

The figures, all in difficult twisted or contracted poses, are rendered with that conspicuous effortlessness that distinguishes Classical art at its best. With masterly economy of line and a sure fluid hand, the artist has flawlessly defined all the bodily forms and gestures, the drapery over Aphrodite's lower limbs, and even something of Pan's hairiness, without the drawing ever becoming fussy or overly detailed. Every line is descriptive, and none redundant. This is line drawing — the art of the cartoon — at its very best, and it yields figures every bit as 'real' as three-dimensional sculpture.

Hinged mirrors of bronze (exceptional examples were made of silver) were invented in Greece in the fifth century BC and became popular in the following century, as feminine taste began to assert itself more conspicuously in articles of daily use. They are essentially like a modern compact, with two discs hinged together. The mirror face, the inner surface of the lower disc, was made slightly convex so as to reflect a larger area. Some fine examples are gilded but most are simply polished bronze. The lid functioned as a protective covering, being curved like the mirror so as not to touch the face except at the very edge. When adjusted to the right angle it could also serve as a reflector, illuminating the user's face.

All surfaces except the mirror itself were usually ornamented, greatest attention being devoted to the cover. In addition to the engraving on the underside, the cover usually had soldered to its top a moulded figural group or floral design. Sometimes details of the cover decoration were added in silver and gold. The back of this mirror carries a three-figure group, perhaps to be identified as Aphrodite (seated on the stool) being crowned by Eros, while a maiden flees. Feminine preferences are apparent in the subjects of both reliefs and engravings; violent mythical or epic scenes are known, but Aphrodite, Eros, Dionysus, love scenes and female heads are much more common. Above all, the ornament had to be decorative.

The effect of the engraving was originally of dark lines on a light, highly polished background — the opposite of the modern effect of white, talc-filled grooves in the corroded, dark-green bronze.

The British Museum mirror is reported to have come from Corinth, a renowned centre of metalworking in the fourth century BC and a major centre of the cult of Aphrodite.

Cupid unstringing his bow

Roman copy of a Classical Greek statue of Eros,
*c.*350 BC, probably by Lysippus
100 BC–AD 100 (Late Republican or Early
Imperial Period)
from the Castello di Guido, near Rome, Italy
marble
62.0 cm height
cat. no. **82**

Cupid has the distinction of being the only pagan deity who also became a standard feature of modern Christian iconography. The chubby winged babies who swarm across Baroque paintings and altar pieces are direct descendants of the Roman god of love, who in turn derives from the Greek love-god Eros.

He was not always so young. In early Classical times Eros seems to have been envisaged as a young man. But by the fourth century BC, as in this sculpture, he had become a boy, and grew younger still in the Hellenistic Period, ending up as the pudgy infant adopted for cherubs by Raphael and the Venetian artists of the Renaissance. Cupid's Christian heirs, of course, lose any connotation of polytheism as they come to take on the role of divine acolytes, fluttering around supporting the major characters and props, or just filling space. But amorini (little loves), as the Cupid figures in overtly pagan scenes are called, clearly retain the amorous character of the Greek god who 'loosens the limbs and damages the mind' (Hesiod), and continue to exploit the power of his darts to inspire passionate love in their unwitting victims.

This sculpture is a Roman work of the late Republican or early Imperial Period, but it copies an earlier Greek work of the fourth century BC. The model was probably a life-size statue of Eros by Lysippus, either the famous bronze image which Pausanias saw at Thespiae in central Greece, or another by the sculptor at Myndos in south-western Turkey. Both of these originals are unfortunately lost.

We can glimpse in this Eros something of the brilliance which made the pre-eminent portraitist of his day — Alexander the Great allowed Lysippus alone to carve his likeness — also one of the great innovators in full-figure sculpture. Lysippus claimed to have had no teacher but Nature herself, and said that while other sculptors made men as they were, he made them as they seemed to be. This was a declaration of what we would call 'naturalism', the attempt to bring art as close as possible to the world of pure appearances. To this end, he introduced a new canon of proportions for the human body, with a somewhat smaller head and less massive frame than the figures of Polyclitus. His figures are still athletic, but their muscles no longer have the exaggerated sharpness of definition that gives some earlier works the air of an anatomy lesson. Cupid is just a boy, but even in Lysippus' adult figures, the musculature is rendered with the same slender fluidity that we see here. The perfect athlete, impervious to the effects of over-indulgence and ageing, has been replaced by a more plausible image of manhood.

Cupid braces the bow against his leg as he strains to undo the string. Such momentary, intrinsically unstable actions seem to have particularly interested Lysippus. Another of his innovations is reflected in Cupid's twisting torso and the wide extension of his arms, gesturing outwards into the space around him. More than any of his predecessors, Lysippus made his figures interact with the surrounding space, embracing it in wide, sweeping movements which break out of the usual static frontal stance or forward stride. This set in train the Hellenistic development towards figures conceived as fully three-dimensional works, to be viewed equally from any angle.

Lysippus' bronze Eros was perfect fodder for Roman copyists who turned out reproductions in large numbers — over forty have survived. The cute treatment of the theme was ideal for the decoration of gardens and villas, where a more overtly religious image would have looked out of place. And the young subject lent itself naturally to small-scale reproductions which could be quickly produced. Marble being more brittle than bronze, figures in this material required the addition of a tree-trunk support by the left leg. This one is draped with a lion skin.

The British Museum Cupid was found in 1776 at Castello di Guido near Rome on the road to Tivoli. The body and wings were buried in a jar which has preserved their surfaces well. The feet, quiver and pedestal, found in the earth nearby, have suffered rather more. The restored sculpture was brought to England by Charles Townley, who bought it from its finder Gavin Hamilton for £60 shortly before 1780.

cat. no. 82

Aphrodite unfastening her sandal

Roman copy of a Greek statue of *c*.300–100 BC
100 BC–AD 100 (Late Republican or Early
Imperial Period)
Italy, findspot unknown
marble
33.7 cm height
cat. no. **83**

The naturalistic revolution in Greek sculpture of the Archaic and Classical Periods
focused almost exclusively on the athletic
male. All major developments in anatomical
realism, variation of stance and the suggestion of movement are first seen in statues
of naked men, whose structured physique
and sharply articulated musculature lent
itself more naturally to these experiments
than a woman's more fluid, continuous form.
The female body served as a convenient
basis for exercises in how clinging drapery
could be used to reveal underlying form, but
it was incidental to the major achievements
of the age.

All this changed with the statue of Aphrodite, carved by Praxiteles around the middle
of the fourth century BC. Showing the love-
goddess completely nude, and abandoning
the upright, four-square stance that had
conditioned the Classical male, Praxiteles'
marble figure created for the first time an
ideal of female beauty which could take its
place beside the athletic male. This Aphrodite
became in time the most celebrated of all
Classical sculptures — the Roman writer
Pliny regarded it as 'superior to anything not
only by Praxiteles, but in the whole world' —
and was reproduced in countless copies.

Praxiteles' statue also inspired a spate of
Hellenistic Aphrodites, showing the goddess
in various poses: standing and squatting,
nude and partially draped, attending to her
hair or necklace, and unfastening her sandal
before bathing. The British Museum statuette is a version of this last type, probably
created in the third or second century BC.
More complete examples allow the scene to
be filled out: the goddess reaches down to
remove her right sandal, while steadying
herself with her left arm. In this, the rarer
version, she grasps her foot behind the axis
of the body; the more common type has her
lifting the leg in front and reaching forward.

Although far from complete — the head,
arms and perhaps the feet were carved
separately and attached with dowels — this
statuette has been much admired since the
eighteenth century for its beautifully sen-
sitive carving. Charles Townley acquired it
from the Italian sculptor and antiquities
restorer Bartolomeo Cavaceppi, who had
kept it in his studio as a model of ancient art
at its best. Praxiteles' Aphrodite was one of
the first statues to exploit marble for its likeness to flesh tones, and the warm, yellowish
stone of this piece certainly enhances the
fine sculpting of the goddess's ample form.
Broad-hipped and small-breasted, she
reflects an ideal of feminine beauty far
removed from today's pin-ups, but by no
means unique to the Greeks — she could
easily take her place among Rubens's
seventeenth-century beauties.

As the embodiment of sexual love and
fertility, Aphrodite was one of the most
widely worshipped of all Greco-Roman
deities. According to Greek tradition, it was
Aphrodite who, by offering Paris the hand of
Helen, tempted him to judge her the most
beautiful of the goddesses and thus sowed
the seed of the Trojan War. True to her
amorous nature, she had various affairs
and off-spring. One of these was Aeneas,
the Trojan hero who eventually settled in
Italy, where his descendant Romulus was
said to have founded Rome. Thus Greek
Aphrodite — or Venus as she was known to
the Romans — became also the special
protectress of Rome.

Statuettes such as this would have been
made for private exhibition indoors. Most of
the innumerable Aphrodites of the Roman
Imperial Period were destined for houses,
though some such images would have
been displayed also in small shrines,
brothels and other places associated with
the goddess.

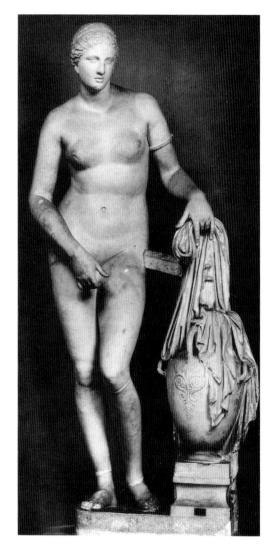

Roman copy of the Knidian Aphrodite by
Praxiteles, *c*.350 BC, Vatican Museum.
(Hirmer Archive)

cat. no. 83

The satyr Marsyas

Greek adaptation of a Classical statue of
*c.*450 BC by the sculptor Myron
100 BC–AD 100 (Roman Period)
Patras, Greece
bronze
76.0 cm height
cat. no. **84**

This nearly half life-size statue shows the ill-fated satyr Marsyas starting back in surprise at a set of musical pipes which the goddess Athena had just thrown down on the ground. According to Greek legend, the goddess herself invented the double flute, but seeing in a pool of water the unflattering effect that blowing into them had on her cheeks, she cast them aside. Marsyas, meanwhile, had been captivated by the sound of Athena's new instrument, and could hardly believe his luck as the pipes now lay before him on the ground. Hastening to pick them up, he was swiftly rebuked by Athena, who warned that the gods' discards should not be touched. But the temptation was more than the wilful satyr could resist and, taking the pipes, Marsyas began to play. Overcome by the mellifluous sounds he was able to produce, the satyr boldly challenged Apollo, the god of music, to a contest. The Muses were duly brought in to judge and Apollo, who could play his lyre upside-down, was deemed the winner. In the grisly climax to the story, Apollo, allowed by the terms of the contest to impose any punishment he wished, had the presumptuous Marsyas skinned alive. Thus the poor creature encountered his nemesis — a peculiarly Greek concept of the retribution that inevitably befell those mortals whose ambition, pride or even happiness exceeded the limits prescribed by the gods.

The British Museum Marsyas was probably made in the first century BC or AD, but it is based on the life-size Marsyas in a two-figure work by the renowned fifth-century BC Athenian sculptor Myron (best known for his *Discus Thrower*) which stood on the Acropolis in Athens. Myron's group (which has not survived) represented the satyr with Athena, who was shown turning back disapprovingly as he comes upon the pipes.

Marsyas is seen abruptly halting as he spies the pipes (not depicted in this version) on the ground. The drama of the simple but perilous event is skilfully captured in his gestures. The outstretched left arm with raised palm graphically evokes his surprise and dismay; while the right hand lifted to the back of the head conveys perfectly the worried thoughtfulness of one who knowingly confronts a fatal dilemma.

Closer copies of Myron's work are in the early Classical Style of the mid-fifth century BC, the muscles sharp and well defined. Here, however, there is a more realistically fluid treatment of the anatomy which, together with the proportions of the body, reflects the influence of the late fourth-century BC sculptor Lysippus (compare cat. no. 82). The treatment of hair and beard, rippling over the chest like cascading water, is likewise a sign of the Hellenistic age, when such techniques were widely exploited for their expressive power.

Satyrs were a very popular subject in Greek vase painting, terracottas and bronze statuettes, but are rarely represented in monumental sculpture before the Hellenistic Period, Myron's group being a notable exception. They were most familiar to Greeks of the Classical Period as bawdy revellers in vase paintings and from 'satyr plays' dramatizing the more ribald aspects of popular legends, in which the chorus would dress up as satyrs. As well as providing an element of light relief, these mischievous man-horse hybrids served as a convenient vehicle for expressing the licentious and hedonistic aspects of human nature. The story of Marsyas, with its weighty moral, was a reminder that even for these fun-loving creatures, disrespect for the gods was perilous.

Marsyas has lost his tail but is otherwise well preserved.

cat. no. **84**

The Greek playwright Sophocles

Hellenistic version of a Greek portrait statue,
probably dating to *c.*325 BC
300–100 BC (Hellenistic Period)
Turkey, findspot unknown (acquired in Istanbul)
bronze
34.8 cm height
cat. no. **85**

Sophocles was one of the three great writers of tragic plays in fifth-century BC Athens, the two others being Aeschylus and Euripides. Living to the grand old age of ninety (496–406 BC), he was said to have written no less than 123 dramas, but of this prodigious output only the seven plays which found their way into a Roman compilation have survived. Thanks largely to one of Sigmund Freud's best known theories, the most famous today is *Oedipus Rex*, in which Sophocles vividly portrays the mounting anguish of the King of Thebes as he discovers that a man he murdered was his own father and the widow he married none other than his mother.

Sophocles' portrait is just as we would imagine the great poet to have looked in old age (about seventy-five?): a wise and noble face, the lean, time-worn features and thoughtfully furrowed brow capturing the serious, public-spirited attitude of the man who, apart from exhorting his fellow citizens to honourable deeds and reminding them of man's ultimate helplessness before the gods, twice served as a military commander. We can detect, too, in his classical features vestiges of those good looks which, at the age of sixteen, had him leading the youthful celebrations of the victory over the Persians at Salamis.

In fact, however, this masterful portrayal is probably bogus. Sophocles died in 406 BC, seventy years before the first recorded statue of him was erected in the Theatre of Dionysus at Athens (though the statue is long lost, the inscribed base survives). Even if a contemporary portrait had been attempted, it would have been an idealized image (like that of Pericles, cat. no. 70) epitomizing the common archetype of the great poet, and only secondarily attuned to Sophocles' actual features. There is, in any case, no evidence that such a work existed, and by the time the statue for the Theatre of Dionysus was created (330s BC), no living sculptor could ever have seen him. What we have, then, is probably a work of the imagination, the style of which reflects the age of its creation rather than the High Classical art of Sophocles' day.

But its importance as evidence of a crucial development in art history remains. The fourth-century BC Sophocles was created just as realism, particularly in portraiture, was starting to emerge as a major preoccupation of Greek artists, and his fictional image owes much to the new sense of individual character with which sculptors were beginning to imbue their works. It was during this period that Lysistratus, the brother of Alexander the Great's portraitist Lysippus, was said to have been the first to take plaster casts of his subjects. The real features of particular individuals thus became the starting point for creating works which copied nature, rather than modifications introduced to lend some semblance of individuality to idealized types.

Fictional or not, the ageing, bearded Sophocles soon became an established image, and was widely reproduced in antiquity. Copyists sometimes introduced stylistic traits of their own day, but the face remained recognizably the same, and it is on this basis that uninscribed examples like the British Museum head have been identified.

Two slightly different types are known and it is unclear which is the version originally set up in Athens around 330 BC. A full-length example of the so-called 'Lateran' Sophocles shows him standing in an enveloping sheet-like garment, on his face the rather bland expression of the archetypal Classical poet. The 'Farnese' type, which may be slightly later, presents a rather older face. All surviving examples are from marble herms (square pillars topped by busts) and do not have the expressive crow-foot wrinkles around the eyes or the deeply furrowed brow of this bronze. The use of such graphic devices to portray age and character are hallmarks of the full-blown realism of Hellenistic times, and for this reason most experts regard this head as an up-dated version of the older-looking 'Farnese' Sophocles, probably made in the third or second century BC.

Of more than fifty known portraits of Sophocles, only one other is made of bronze. Because casting-moulds for metal images could be taken from the finest available sculptures, these bronzes probably give the best idea of the quality of the lost originals. The eyes were originally inlaid.

The modern history of the British Museum Sophocles begins in Constantinople (Istanbul), where it was bought in the early seventeenth century for Thomas Howard, Earl of Arundel (1585–1646). Intrigued by Classical antiquities before they had become more widely fashionable, Arundel amassed the first great collection of ancient art in England. Although incorrectly identified as Homer, the head's artistic merit was apparent to all, and it was regarded as one of his finest acquisitions.

cat. no. **85**

Companion of Odysseus

Roman copy of a full-length Greek statue of c.AD 50–100
c.AD 120 (Imperial Period)
from Hadrian's villa, Tivoli, near Rome, Italy
marble
58.8 cm height

cat. no. **86**

Of the many new themes and priorities which emerged in the figurative arts in the Hellenistic Period, one of the most conspicuous and fundamental was the interest in individuals as visually unique and distinctive subjects. Closely connected with this was a belated revival of interest in the inner life of the subject — showing mood and feelings through facial expression — and in the dramatic effects of tousled hair and fluttering drapery. The sculptors of the Classical Period, who managed to render so well the body in all its various positions and movements, for some reason shied away from imitating the facial expressions to match. Classical figures do battle, play sport, meet their gruesome deaths or stand idly by, all with the same air of passionless detachment.

In the Hellenistic Period, sculpture comes vividly to life as individual character and the expression of immediate emotion become the focus of innovative work. Mouths open, brows furrow and eyes roll heavenward in dramatic — often melodramatic — expressions of fear, anger or pathetic hope. Pathos and drama are the keynotes of the period, and subjects were chosen accordingly: battles and contests, great epic heroes, the victims of tragic fate, the very young and the very old. This is art with an overtly emotive basis, a weighty sentimentality that has led modern scholars to liken it to the Baroque movement in seventeenth-century Italy. Hellenistic art at its best is moving in a way that Classical art never can be; its graphic emotionalism strikes a more immediate and more human chord.

The bust shown here is in this 'Baroque' style of the late third and early second centuries BC, known as 'Pergamene' after the capital of the Attalid Kingdom in western Turkey, where many of the finest sculptors worked. But it was not itself carved in that period; nor is it a copy of a piece carved then. It is a second-century AD copy of a first-century AD original which mimicked the earlier Baroque style.

How can original works be distinguished so emphatically from those of copyists at various removes? Usually they cannot. Some Roman copyists were very good indeed, and they make the dating of individual sculptures very difficult. In this case, however, evidence which not only allows the work to be dated, but also establishes its subject and makers, came to light in 1957 when four groups of marble statues were found in a coastal grotto at Sperlonga, south of Rome. The two major groups show the Greek hero Odysseus (Ulysses) and his companions in their wanderings after the Trojan War. In one group Odysseus and three companions are shown blinding the one-eyed giant Cyclops, who had captured them in his cave and intended to devour one each day.

One of the figures of this group was the model for our bust. Over two metres tall, it shows a companion holding an empty wineskin which the sleeping Cyclops has drunk. As Odysseus and two other companions prepare to thrust a pointed stake into the monster's giant eye, our figure, his head turned towards the victim with an expression of faintly disguised panic, prepares to flee.

The names of the sculptors inscribed on the other Odysseus group — a famous trio known from ancient writers — allows it to be dated with reasonable confidence to the late first century AD, and this may be taken as the likely date of the Cyclops group also, since it is carved in the same style and type of stone. Our head, carefully copied from the Sperlonga figure, even down to the individual locks of hair, was carved for the emperor Hadrian in about AD 120 to decorate his villa at Tivoli, where it was found in 1771.

The head came to the British Museum among the collection of Charles Townley, who had bought it for £200 — a phenomenal price he later regretted. It was restored, probably in the eighteenth century, repairing damage to the lips and nose, and setting it in its present bust.

Companion of Odysseus, from a group showing the blinding of the Cyclops, late first century AD, Sperlonga, Italy. (Prof. Dr W. Andreae)

cat. no. **86**

The wine-god Bacchus

Roman copy of a Greek statue of Dionysus, c.300–200 BC
c.AD 100–150 (Imperial Period)
from The 'Caesareum', Cyrene, Libya
marble
1.72 m height
cat. no. 87

The vine wreath and bunch of grapes held by this life-size marble figure identify it immediately as the Greek wine-god Dionysus, known to the Romans as Bacchus. One of the most widely worshipped of all Greco-Roman gods, Dionysus–Bacchus featured with other major deities in official religious ceremonies and celebrations, but it was as a major force in popular religion — the private cults of the masses — that his great following developed. This appeal stemmed not so much from his association with wine as from the more mystical and ecstatic aspects of the Dionysian cult, which apparently appealed particularly to women. He became connected also with the netherworld, ensuring the survival of the dead in Hades. The secret ceremonies or 'mysteries' of Dionysus (the Roman Bacchanalia) — illustrated on cat. no. 93 — involved orgiastic rites in which the initiated would work themselves into ecstatic trances. Women in this hysterical condition were said to run through the woods tearing apart and devouring any animals unfortunate enough to cross their paths.

The worship of Dionysus spread from Greece to southern Italy and Rome. In 186 BC the Senate attempted to outlaw the Bacchanalia, but to no avail. The god's following only increased in the late Republic and into Imperial times, when this statue was carved.

The long hair, soft, fluid physique and languid stance of the god reflect the increasingly effeminate terms in which Dionysus and certain other male gods (particularly Apollo and the youthful Eros) were conceived in Hellenistic and Roman times. The trend towards a softer, younger, more sensuous image of these deities had its origins in the fourth century BC, when the previous tendency for women to be rendered with boyish hips and shoulders was reversed, and the female form began to suffuse the male physique. These developments do not reflect changing moral or philosophical views so much as the search for new artistic challenges. The preoccupation of Archaic and early Classical artists with anatomical analysis had favoured the hard, clear lines of the athletic male body. But as the Classical Period progressed and the male form was mastered, interest shifted to the softer forms and subtler transitions of the female form (see cat. no. 83). The ultimate outcome of this stylistic transsexualism is seen in the Hellenistic hermaphrodites, figures with a woman's hips and breasts but male genitals. Dionysus never reached that ambiguous extreme, but his masculinity has been clearly compromised in statues like this, with its beardless face, smooth, fleshy body and languid stance. It evokes nothing of Dionysus the famous warrior and conqueror, only the handsome young lover of Ariadne — a role which was increasingly emphasized in Hellenistic Dionysian narrative art.

The immediate model for this new divine type seems to have been the love-goddess Aphrodite. She is often shown, like Dionysus here, with long flowing locks of hair and a swathe of drapery across the hips dipping just enough to suggest her sexuality.

The Bacchus was found in 1860 or 1861 by British officers stationed in Malta, who took to digging for antiquities among the ruins of the large Roman city at Cyrene in north Africa. The Bacchus was found with a limestone panther in a temple of the wine-god, but subsequent research has shown that the enclosure in which the building stood was dedicated to the deified Roman dictator Julius Caesar. Except for the loss of the right arm, which probably held a small wine jug, the statue was in remarkably good condition, 'the surface being almost without a scratch', as the excavators remarked. They also noticed traces of red paint on the eyes and wreath, rare evidence of the colouring which most Greek and Roman statues originally bore. It was made in the early second century AD, probably as part of a major rebuilding of Cyrene (which had suffered damage in a Jewish revolt) under the emperor Hadrian.

The Roman emperor Augustus

The Blacas-Strozzi Cameo
c.AD 10–20 (Early Imperial Period); diadem
added in the Medieval Period
(Italy ?), findspot unknown
sardonyx
12.8 x 9.3 cm
cat. no. **88**

The famous Blacas-Strozzi Cameo (so named after its previous owners) bears a near-contemporary portrait of one of the pivotal figures of ancient history: the Roman emperor Augustus (ruled 27 BC–AD 14). As the great-nephew and adoptive heir of Julius Caesar, the young Octavian (as he was then known) took it upon himself to avenge Caesar's brutal murder, and soon established himself as a leading force in the intrigue-ridden politics of the late Republic. With his victories over Antony and Cleopatra in 31–30 BC, Octavian became undisputed master of Rome. Honours and privileges were thrust upon him, changing forever the face of Roman politics. In 27 BC he was granted the title 'Augustus' and became by common consent the *princeps* or 'first citizen'. Although his position continued in theory to depend on senatorial support — in the same year he had ceremoniously 'restored' the Republic — in practice his wealth and influence brought absolute power. Modern historians acknowledge the fiction which the Republic had now become by beginning Rome's Imperial Period at this point.

Like the Greek monarchs of the Hellenistic Period, the Roman emperors gathered together the finest artists of the day — still overwhelmingly Greeks — in state workshops, where they produced jewellery, gold and silver plate, as well as other luxury items, for the imperial household. Augustus' personal gem cutter was Dioscorides, some of whose signed intaglio gems have survived.

Among the most luxurious products of the imperial workshops was a series of 'state cameos' showing the emperors and their families, sometimes in the company of gods. Augustus' surviving cameos, some of which were probably carved by Dioscorides (though none is signed), were among the finest of all. The example shown here carries an exquisitely carved bust of the emperor wearing military dress and bearing a spear. Like the Hellenistic monarchs, he wears a diadem (the original was carved away for the bejewelled medieval overlay); and over his shoulder he bears the scaly cape (*aegis*) of Jupiter (with whom Augustus was posthumously identified), a goatskin fringed by snakes and bearing the heads of Medusa, the gorgon-monster, and the bearded Phobos (Fear). On public monuments neither of these features would have been acceptable to Romans, who had a deep distrust of monarchy, but in private works imperial artists could be less inhibited.

As a portrait, this profile is of limited value. Like Augustus' public portraits, it has been highly idealized in accordance with the Classicizing revival he promoted. His images — especially in sculpture — are closer to the gods of fifth-century Athens than to the care-worn faces of Pompey, Caesar and their contemporaries, or to the description of him given by Suetonius:

> He had clear bright eyes ... few teeth, which were small and dirty ... his hair was yellowish and slightly curly, his eyebrows met and his nose jutted out and then turned inwards ... He was ... rather short, but with well-proportioned limbs. On his body were spots, birthmarks and calluses caused by excessive use of the strigil [for scraping off oil]. He sometimes limped and suffered generally from a weak constitution.

This all-too-human appearance has here been transformed into an ageless image of the ideal hero: serene, confident and all-powerful.

Augustus' youthfulness is partly responsible for the startlingly different quality of his portraits. The leading figures of the previous generation had been experienced elder statesmen; he, on the other hand, was little more than a youth, whose fresh features lent themselves naturally to a more Classical treatment. But there was also a deeper cause rooted in the novelty of Augustus' position: his concern to appear as the upholder of traditional Roman values and virtues. To embody these values in art, he settled upon the style which both epitomized the greatest achievement of the past and best expressed the authority and dignity appropriate to the imperial persona. Casting their gods in the image of the idealized man, Greek artists of the fifth century BC had created a bridge between the mortal and the divine which suited perfectly the ruler who, as Julius Caesar's adopted heir, was considered the son of a god, and was himself worshipped as a deity in remoter parts of the empire.

The bichrome effect of the cameo depends on the regular horizontal banding of the sardonyx. The removal of the white around the head makes it stand out boldly against the dark brown of the underlying layer. An upper layer of brown is exploited as colouring for the cape.

The cameo technique was a relatively late invention of the third century BC; most were made to be worn as pendants. The Blacas-Strozzi Cameo is usually assumed to have been carved during Augustus' lifetime (died AD 14), but it may date to the reign of his successor Tiberius (AD 14–37).

cat. no. 88

Octavia, sister of the Roman emperor Augustus

Cameo portraying Octavia as the goddess Diana with hunting spear; perhaps carved by Solon
*c.*20 BC (Early Imperial Period)
findspot unknown
agate
5.6 x 4.6 cm
cat. no. 89

Although Roman emperors were not usually declared gods until after death, they were sometimes represented with divine attributes. The mighty Augustus was shown wearing Jupiter's cape (cat. no. 88) or with the god's eagle at his feet; Commodus had himself sculpted with Hercules' club and lion skin; and the megalomaniacal Nero regularly affected divinity in his hairstyle and general demeanour — so successfully, indeed, that a gigantic bronze statue of the emperor was later rededicated as an image of the sun-god Helios.

The emperor's immediate family also could be portrayed in the guise of deities. The subject of this gem is identified by the hunting spear as Diana (Greek Artemis), the virgin goddess of the woods and hunting. But it is also a veiled portrait of a member of the imperial household, probably Augustus' sister Octavia, the mother of Antonia (cat. no. 90). This identification is based not so much on the woman's features — which are highly idealized — as on the existence of a companion piece, of the same dimensions, stone and style. This matching bust, facing in the opposite direction, shows the emperor Augustus as Mercury (Greek Hermes) with the god's distinctive herald's wand (*caduceus*) before him, in the same position as Diana's spear. Rather than pendants, these two masterly gems may have been displayed side by side as an antithetical pair, set up in some way that exploited the translucent quality of the thin-cut stone. The exceptional quality of the carving suggests the hand of Solon, one of the finest engravers of Augustan times.

The goddess has the Classical features popularized by Augustus' court artists (compare cat. no. 90). Her hair is plaited and tied around the front of the head, delicate tresses falling over her forehead, temple and the nape of her neck. The revealing dress, buttoned along the arm, falls seductively from the shoulder. The carving of the youthful profile and hair is exquisite. Only the mechanical roundness of the near breast, executed in the conventional manner by drilling, strikes an unhappy note in what is otherwise a sublime example of the Roman engraver's art.

Octavia was much admired by her contemporaries for her loyalty, humanity and nobility, traditional feminine Roman virtues which she was able to maintain while many around her succumbed to intrigue and treachery. In 40 BC Octavia was married to Mark Antony to cement his political alliance with her brother Augustus, but Antony divorced her when that pact broke down. Despite rejection and Antony's subsequent death, Octavia continued to bring up all his children — including their own two daughters and those born to him later by Cleopatra — as well as her three children by a previous marriage.

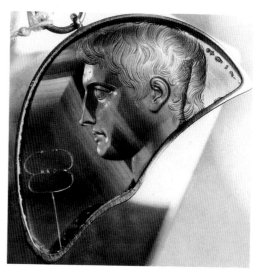

The emperor Augustus as Mercury, with the god's messenger-wand. (R.L. Wilkins, courtesy Prof. Sir John Boardman)

cat. no. 89

Antonia, niece of the Roman emperor Augustus

Roman portrait bust
c.AD 30 (Early Imperial Period)
Italy, findspot unknown
marble
68.5 cm height
cat. no. **90**

The Greek Classical Style of official art sponsored by the emperor Augustus (see cat. nos 88, 89) set the pattern for much of the imperial portraiture of the next century. Not only the emperor but also his family were often presented in the flawless, ageless mould of the fifth-century BC Greek god or goddess. Such is the young woman portrayed in this bust. Her smooth, subtle features; the wavy hair gathered at the back; the dress buttoned along the shoulder — all are unmistakable links with the goddesses of Classical times. The reality, however, may have been very different.

The identification of such an idealized image inevitably presents difficulties — so much so that putting names to Julio-Claudian portraits has become a small industry among Roman art historians. The Classical Style and fine quality of the carving assure her imperial status, and comparisons with more securely identified portraits suggest in particular Antonia (36 BC–AD 37), the daughter of Mark Antony and Octavia (cat. no. 89), and mother of the emperor Claudius. Although shown here through the age-defying Classical looking-glass as a young woman, the bust was probably carved in Antonia's mature years, perhaps in the last few months of her life when the new emperor Caligula showered his ageing grandmother with honours. His respect for the matriarch of the family proved short-lived however, and it was Caligula's anger at her criticisms that soon after drove Antonia to suicide.

The nickname 'Clytie', by which this piece is often known, refers to the nymph who was spurned by the sun-god Helios and turned into a flower. Here, however, the petals around the bottom are just a decorative border. The bust is exceptional in being almost perfectly intact; only small parts of the left ear and the back of the head are missing.

But what we see today is not entirely original, for there seems to have been some reworking of the surface in the eighteenth century. Early collectors were not above employing able artists to 'improve' their ancient sculptures by judicious recarving. The culprit in this case was probably Prince Laurenzano of Naples, who sold the bust to Charles Townley in 1772 for £95.

'Clytie' became Townley's favourite piece (it is shown on his desk in Zoffany's painting, p. 13), and the story was told that when his London house was threatened during the Gordon riots of 1780, Townley 'secured his cabinet of gems, and was taking, as he then feared, a last view of his marbles, when he seized the bust above-mentioned, and hurried with it to his carriage', exclaiming, 'I must take care of my wife!'.

cat. no. **90**

The flight of Icarus and Daedalus

Roman wall-painting
before AD 79 (Imperial Period)
from a villa near Pompeii, Italy
painted plaster
35.5 x 34.5 cm height
cat. no. **91**

Late in the morning of 24 August in the year AD 79, the mountain of Vesuvius, fifteen kilometres south-east of Naples, came to life. There had been tremors in previous days, but this time the mountain erupted with a ferocity that left people frozen in their tracks. An eye-witness account of the horrifying event is provided by Pliny the Younger, whose uncle commanded the local fleet. He tells of heavy carts being thrown around on the ground as the sea retreated from the shore; how there appeared 'a horrible black cloud ripped by sudden bursts of fire, writhing snake-like'; how the terrified inhabitants were enveloped by 'an ominous thick smoke, spreading over the earth like a flood' and plunging them into 'the darkness of a sealed room without lights'. Many died, asphyxiated by the scorching fumes and ashes, but Pliny and his mother luckily avoided the thickest falls and made it through alive. When the ash clouds dissolved 'before [their] terror-stricken gaze everything appeared changed — covered by a thick layer of ashes like an abundant snowfall'. Pompeii was buried under more than five metres of pumice and ash. And so it remained until treasure hunters began to explore its ruins in the 1740s.

Pompeii's misfortune was archaeology's great boon. Here was an entire Roman town, frozen in time by a natural disaster that gave the 20 000 inhabitants no time to collect their belongings, and many were not even able to escape. The eruption, ten times as powerful as that of Mount St Helens in Washington State, USA, in 1980, sent ash and pumice twenty kilometres into the sky and showered rocks of up to twenty centimetres for kilometres around. Ground surges of gases and ash raced down the mountain at speeds of over one hundred kilometres per hour, followed by ash flows which burned wood to temperatures of 750 degrees Farenheit. Many people seem to have thought

their only hope lay by sea; many bodies have recently been found crowded into the marina at the nearby town of Herculaneum, which was also buried in the eruption.

The walls of many of the houses of Pompeii were decorated with elaborate paintings which provide a rare insight into this most fragile and easily ruined of all the major arts. Ranging from the second century BC to the years before AD 79, they vary greatly in subject and style, and much effort has been devoted to their chronological and stylistic groupings. The panel shown here, from a villa near Pompeii, illustrates the story of Icarus and his father Daedalus, the legendary master-craftsman who worked for King Minos of Crete. Imprisoned for helping Theseus slay the Minotaur bull-monster, the ever-resourceful Daedalus contrived an escape for himself and his son by making wings of birds' feathers, which he attached to their shoulders with wax. But Icarus ignored his father's warning not to fly too close to the sun and the wax of his wings melted. The painting shows him plunging headlong into the sea, watched in horror by a shepherd (perhaps the god Pan), two women on a headland and the passengers of a passing boat. A small temple and a tree occupy a promontory to the left, and in the background we see a rocky island and a walled town with an amphitheatre. The Romans did not properly understand perspective drawing, and the reasonably consistent perspective of the lower half of the picture is completely thrown out by the almost aerial view of the distant town. Another technical error, perhaps the result of the hasty painting style, is the mismatched reflection of the temple in the water below.

The emphasis on landscape in scenes like this represented a new departure in Classical art. Landscape had been largely incidental to Greek painting, whose grand masters concentrated on achieving realistic effects of space and form through architectural perspective and careful shading and highlights. Landscape was to them essentially a backdrop, to be elaborated no more than was necessary to set the scene.

The painters of Pompeian mythological landscapes turned this tradition upside-down. Here the landscape is everything and the actors incidental. Reduced to diminutive proportions, the figures are dwarfed by their setting and treated in the same way as trees, rocks and other elements of the landscape. No longer singled out for special attention, they become one with their environment, in danger at times of being lost in the broad swathes of colour and light.

And therein lies the other and more obviously revolutionary aspect of Roman wall-painting, at least to the twentieth-century eye: the strikingly modern quality of what can only be called its impressionistic approach. The careful outlining of form and the modelling of mass by hatching — techniques which had been the backbone of Greek painting — were largely abandoned by the Pompeian landscape painters. They worked instead with rapidly applied dabs of colour, often no more than rough approximations of the true shape of things, which attempted to mimic the play of light and dark, creating the impression of a scene glimpsed fleetingly through half-closed eyes. Figures and elements of landscape alike are reduced to abbreviated squiggles, their forms open and ill-defined.

Called *ars compendiaria* ('abbreviated' or 'short-cut' art) by the Romans, some aspects of the Pompeian landscape style may have grown out of Hellenistic wall-painting, of which much less evidence survives. A quick, sketchy, linear brushstroke — more drawing than painting — is already apparent in some late Greek work. But Pompeian artists used the technique in a way no Greek had contemplated — not so much to define the forms of things, as to convey the play of light on their surfaces. They realized that if the tonal chemistry of light and dark could be got right, the shapes would define themselves. It is this that distinguishes the Roman painters so clearly from their predecessors and unites them across a gap of nearly 2000 years with the Impressionists of modern times.

A vandal by the name of Donatos left his mark across the painting in antiquity.

cat. no. **91**

The Roman emperor Antoninus Pius

Roman portrait bust
c.AD 140–175 (Imperial Period)
from the 'House of Jason Magnus', Cyrene, Libya
marble
71.0 cm height
cat. no. 92

It was not until the late eighteenth century that connoisseurs began to distinguish original Greek sculptures in any rigorous way from the much more numerous Roman copies. The existence of these copies was itself testimony to the dependence of Roman art on Greek models; and even when Roman artists were not directly imitating, it was clear that the stylistic seeds of their art lay mostly in Greek soil. As the magnitude of Rome's debt to the Greek genius became apparent, it was inevitable that Roman art should have suffered some loss of prestige. The Greeks, so it seemed to these early critics, were all innovation and inspiration, while the Romans were essentially copyists — a mere postscript to the Greek achievement.

There was something in this view. The Greeks not only created the first fully naturalistic art in history, they also explored the obvious avenues of expressive variation within these new guidelines. Between the cold, passionless idealism of the Classical Period and the graphic realism and turgid emotionalism of Hellenistic art, there was little new ground to be broken. Anything Roman artists did with the human body was bound to draw on the Greek legacy; naturalistic art from now on could not but follow in their footsteps. The Greek achievement could hardly be ignored, but neither was it clear how it could be surpassed.

Yet this was not the whole story. There were areas which the Greeks had not exhausted and which the Romans subsequently stamped as their own. Perhaps the most important of these was portraiture.

The increasing realism of Greek art in the Hellenistic Period was admitted only grudgingly to royal portraiture. Hellenistic monarchs ruled as semi-divine heroes, and their images were contrived above all to convey the dignity and authority of royal status. More often than not, objective realism would make the king look just like the next man — hardly the image an ambitious monarch wanted to project.

The Romans of the Republican Period took a very different view. For them, truth and fidelity were as obviously virtues in art as they were in life. Portraits of the period — even those of prominent figures like Cicero and Caesar — are therefore often uncompromisingly realistic, taking their cue from the wax death-masks which were kept by noble families. These masks, accurately preserving images of the faces of the deceased, seem to have played a key role in the emergence of super-realism ('verism') in Roman portrait sculpture. In this way a tradition of portraiture was established in which the person's actual features formed the artist's primary point of reference — profoundly different from the approach of the Greek portraitists, still constrained as they were by more or less idealized types.

In the Roman world, imperial portrait sculptures were the chief means by which an emperor's likeness was made known and his authority manifested throughout the empire. In eastern provinces, where Oriental notions of divine kingship lingered on, they formed the focus of emperor cults, and casting down such a statue was an act of treachery.

This bust of Antoninus Pius (born AD 86, ruled AD 138–161) conveys well the conscientious but rather colourless person which ancient writers show him to have been. Antoninus was in many ways the model emperor: diligent, fair-minded and respectful — hence the epithet 'Pius' which the Senate bestowed on him. His successor, the philosophically-minded Marcus Aurelius, records his many virtues:

> Gentleness and unshaken resolution in judgement taken after full examination; no vainglory about external honours; love of work and perseverance; readiness to hear those who had anything to contribute to the public advantage; the desire to award to every man according to desert without partiality.

The empire which Antoninus inherited from Hadrian represented the highpoint of Roman power. He made no attempt to further expand the frontiers — it was said that 'he would rather save a single citizen than slay a thousand foes' — never leaving Italy after becoming emperor. But already there were rumbles of discontent around the fringes of the empire, and not long after his death the barbarian invasions which would eventually bring Rome to the verge of destruction began. For the time being, however, Rome prospered. 'The man who splits a cumin seed' left the treasury as rich as it had ever been.

The bust, showing Antoninus in military dress, represents the official portrait which also appears on coins throughout his reign. The emperor wears a cuirass with leather shoulder-straps over a tunic, all covered by a military cloak which is fastened at the shoulder with a brooch. The perfectly preserved face allows us to appreciate what must have been a fairly faithful likeness by a highly accomplished sculptor. Hadrian had set a fashion for beards which Antoninus and his successors — 'the hairy emperors' — continued. The flesh areas have been polished to a porcelain-like lustre, accentuating the contrast with the rich, thickly textured hair. Upward glancing eyes and heavy eyelids — traits that were further exaggerated in portraits of Antoninus' successors — give the emperor a drowsy, languishing air. The hollowed pupils and incised irises are another legacy of Hadrianic times, an aspect of the growing desire to achieve dramatic effects of light and dark by hollowing out and undercutting the stone with a drill. In the following decades this technique was exploited to great effect for hair curls. Traces of paint on the beard suggest that the bust was originally coloured.

The bust of Antoninus was found in a grand official residence (the 'House of Jason Magnus') at Cyrene, the capital of the north African province, along with portraits of two other Antonine emperors and Hadrian. This and other circumstances of its discovery suggest that the sculpture was probably carved posthumously, soon after the emperor's death in AD 161. Details of the carving technique indicate that it is local work, but the quality matches up to the highest Roman standards.

cat. no. **92**

The Mildenhall Great Dish

Roman picture-plate
*c.*AD 360 (Late Imperial Period)
near Mildenhall, Suffolk, England
silver
60.5 cm diameter; 8256 g weight
cat. no. 93

This spectacular dish is widely regarded as one of the finest surviving specimens of Roman silverware. It is the prize piece of a hoard of thirty-two objects found by a farmer in a field near Mildenhall in Suffolk, England, in 1942. Only centimetres below the surface, it had remained undiscovered for some 1600 years, and is only known today because the farmer set his plough to dig ten centimetres deeper than usual.

The decoration of the Mildenhall Dish is among the most lavish and exuberant of all surviving antique metalwork. The bearded face of a sea-god — Neptune or Oceanus — stares out from the centre of the dish, his hair a mass of seaweed and dolphins. Around this medallion a narrow frieze bears three scantily clad Nereids (daughters of another sea-deity Nereus) riding on sea-monsters which have long, coiled tails and the foreparts of a deer, a horse and a man. A fourth Nereid, on a grotesque horned monster, is being lured away by a half-human Triton.

The main interest of the dish, however, lies in the broad frieze of Bacchic revellers that takes up the rest of the interior surface. Details aside, the flamboyant imagery is still essentially Hellenistic in style. The principal characters of the scene are the wine-god Bacchus and Hercules, accompanied by Pan, Silenus, satyrs and maenads. The youthful Bacchus, standing with his foot on a panther and holding a bunch of grapes and a *thyrsus*-staff, strikes a proud and triumphant figure — as well he might, having just worsted Hercules in a drinking contest. The massive frame of the defeated hero is shown four figures to the right, supported by a pair of satyrs as he collapses in a drunken stupor over his lion skin and club. Silenus, an old dwarfish satyr, approaches Bacchus bowl-in-hand, probably offering wine to the god rather than requesting more for himself; while behind Bacchus the man-goat figure of Pan leaps nimbly over a bag of fruit, grasping his distinctive pipes. Around the rest of the frieze maenads and satyrs dance and make merry to the sound of pipes, tambourines and cymbals. Maenads throw their heads back as they swirl around in ecstatic celebration of the wine-god's mystical powers, urged on by the troop of eager satyrs, one of whom wields a curved hunting stick. A surprising lapse by the silversmith (or perhaps deliberate simplification) has left one of the satyrs who support Hercules without any lower body or legs.

Vessels of gold and silver were far the most valuable and highly prized of all dining services in antiquity. Infinitely more expensive than pottery, pieces like this were the preserve of the rich and powerful — emperors, high officials and aristocrats — and would be ostentatiously displayed at banquets and other festive occasions. Most large picture-plates of this kind were probably not used as platters at all — some bear images which it would have been almost blasphemous to obscure under piles of fruit — but mounted on walls, much as fine porcelain or metal plate is still displayed today. Bacchic scenes of drinking and merry-making were a favourite theme, designed to put guests in the right frame of mind. On this dish the combination of motifs may also contain more serious allusions: Oceanus recalling the Islands of the Blessed; the Nereids on their sea-monsters representing the journey of souls across the ocean to the after-life; and the Bacchic revel alluding to the bliss of souls in paradise. When such pieces came into the possession of Christians (as the Mildenhall Dish may have done), instead of being melted down as idolatrous abominations, they seem often to have been reinterpreted in Christian terms. Despite the brazenly pagan images in which the passage to the after-life is allegorized, the scenes on the Mildenhall Dish may have been made acceptable to the Christian owner by regarding them as illustrations of the journey of the soul to heaven.

Turning up in Britain, such superb silverwork in purely Roman-Hellenistic style can only have belonged to a rich and important member of the imperial administration. A clue to its owner may lie in the name Eutherios, which is scratched in Greek on the undersides of two smaller plates from the treasure. The Roman emperor Julian (AD 360–363), famous as 'the Apostate' who reverted from Christianity to paganism, had a close adviser of that name. Although this Eutherios — an Armenian eunuch — apparently got no closer to Britain than Gaul (France), the treasure may possibly have been a gift from him to someone stationed there. If so, a likely recipient is the Christian general Lupicinus who was sent to Britain in AD 360 by Julian (then still a sub-emperor [*Caesar*] of the Gallic provinces) to stem an imminent invasion of Scots, Picts and other barbarians. Lupicinus' Christianity is important, for some spoons from the treasure bear the Chi-Rho monogram (✗), a common early Christian symbol made by superimposing the first two letters of the name 'Christ' in Greek. While Lupicinus was in Britain, Julian was hailed as full emperor (*Augustus*) by his troops and openly declared his paganism. Compelled by his faith to support the legitimate Christian emperor Constantius II, Lupicinus would have been a clear threat to Julian, who duly had him arrested immediately upon his return to Gaul. This worrying turn of events might well have inspired Lupicinus' family or entourage in Britain to secure their treasures in a safe place.

Where Eutherios (or whoever was its original owner) had the Mildenhall Treasure made is now impossible to say, since none of it bears a regional hallmark like some fine silver of the day. Constantinople (modern Istanbul), the city chosen by Constantine the Great for his residence and soon to become the capital of the Roman Empire, was perhaps the pre-eminent metalworking centre of the day; but there were also a number of other cities throughout the empire which produced very fine plate, from Antioch in Syria to Milan in Italy and Trier in Germany.

cat. no. **93**

Time-line

BC	MESOPOTAMIA		EGYPT	
4000		Growth of urban settlements in Sumer	PREDYNASTIC PERIOD	
	URUK PERIOD	First 'cities', writing, cylinder seals		
3000	JEMDET NASR PERIOD	Proto-Elamite writing in Persia		Unification of the 'Two Lands'
				First hieroglyphic writing
	SUMERIAN EARLY	Gilgamesh · First historical inscriptions	ARCHAIC PERIOD	
2500	DYNASTIC PERIOD	Sumerian 'city-states' · 'Royal Cemetery' at Ur		Step pyramid of Djoser
		Cuneiform writing and culture at Ebla (Syria)		Great pyramids at Giza
	AKKADIAN PERIOD	*Sargon*	OLD KINGDOM	First experiments in mummification
				Formation of canonical Egyptian style in art
2000	UR III PERIOD	Sumerian 'Renaissance'	1ST INTERMEDIATE	Breakdown of central power
		Establishment of Amorite and Hurrian states	PERIOD	
	OLD BABYLONIAN	Standardization of cuneiform literature		'Realistic' royal portraits
	PERIOD	*Hammurabi* Law code	MIDDLE KINGDOM	
1500		Hittite sack of Babylon	2ND INTERMEDIATE	Invasion and occupation by Hyksos from Syro-Palestine
	KASSITE PERIOD	Kassite invasion of Babylonia	PERIOD	'Classical' Egyptian style in art
				Temples at Karnak and Luxor (Thebes)
		Assyrian conquest of Babylon	NEW KINGDOM	*Amenophis I Hatshepsut Tuthmosis III Amenophis I*
1000		Elamite sack of Babylon		*Akhenaten Tutankhamun Ramesses II*
	MIDDLE ASSYRIAN/	Aramean invasions · Assyrian decline		'Sea-peoples' repelled
	BABYLONIAN PERIOD	Spread of Aramean language	3RD INTERMEDIATE	Widespread looting of Theban tombs; mummy caches
800		Assyrian revival *Ashurnasirpal II*	PERIOD	Invasion of Palestine *Sheshonq*
700	NEO-ASSYRIAN PERIOD	*Tiglath-Pileser III Sennacherib*		
		Sack of Babylon *Ashurbanipal*		Revival of 'realistic' portraiture
600	NEO-BABYLONIAN	Conquest of Assyria by Medes and Persians		Assyrian invasions
	PERIOD	*Nebuchadnezzar II*	LATE PERIOD	
500		Persian capture of Babylon		Persian conquest
		Cyrus the Great		
	PERSIAN (ACHAEMENID)	*Darius the Great*		Expulsion of Persians
	PERIOD			
400				
300		Conquest of Near East by *Alexander the Great*		Second Persian conquest
		Wars of the Successors		*Alexander the Great* hailed as pharaoh
		Seleucus I	GRECO-ROMAN	Wars of the Successors *Ptolemy I*
		Antiochus I	PERIOD	*Ptolemy II*
	HELLENISTIC PERIOD		Seleucid Empire		Introduction of Greek language and culture
200				
100		Conquest of Mesopotamia by Parthians		
		Decline of cuneiform culture		
	PARTHIAN PERIOD			
AD 1				
100				
200				
300				
400				

THE GREEK WORLD		THE ROMAN WORLD		BC
				4000
				3000
				2500
DDLE BRONZE AGE	Minoan civilization: Palace of Knossos Mycenaean civilization: Palace of Mycenae	BRONZE AGE		2000
				1500
TE BRONZE AGE	Mycenaeans in Cyprus			
OMETRIC PERIOD	Trojan War? Alphabet adopted from Phoenicians *Homer?*			1000
RIENTALIZING PERIOD	Greek colonies established around Mediterranean Orientalizing Style in art · First life-size marble statues	IRON AGE	'Villanovan' settlement at Rome	800
			Traditional foundation of Rome by *Romulus*	700
			Greek colonies in southern Italy, Sicily	
CHAIC PERIOD	*Solon Peisistratus* Invention of red-figure pottery *Cleisthenes*		Widespread Phoenician trade Orientalizing Period in Etruscan art Etruscan kings rule Rome	600
				500
	Persian invasions repelled *Pericles* 'Golden Age' of Athens *Phidias*		Etruscans expelled from Rome · Foundation of Republic Roman conquest of central and southern Italy	
ASSICAL PERIOD	Parthenon built *Polyclitus* Peloponnesian War			
	Socrates Defeat of Athens by Sparta *Plato*			400
	Aristotle Praxiteles Alexander the Great			
	Conquest of Persian Empire *Lysippus*			300
	Spread of Greek culture across Near East	REPUBLICAN PERIOD		
LLENISTIC PERIOD	Wars of the Successors *Euclid*		First Punic (Carthaginian) War	
	Pergamene Style Development of portraiture		Second Punic War *Hannibal* Conquest of Macedonia	200
	Roman sack of Corinth Greek art shipped to Rome		Third Punic War · Destruction of Carthage	
OMAN PERIOD	Neo-Attic workshops established Hellenistic Kingdoms of eastern Mediterranean absorbed by Rome (second to first century BC)		Pergamum becomes a Roman province Republican portraiture *Cicero* Assassination of *Julius Caesar* *Octavian* defeats *Antony* and *Cleopatra* *Octavian* declared 'Augustus' · Roman Empire *Augustus* Classicizing Style in state art	100

				AD 1
		IMPERIAL PERIOD	*Tiberius* *Caligula* *Claudius* Conquest of Britain begun *Nero* Burning of Rome Pompeii destroyed by Vesuvius · Colosseum dedicated	
			Hadrian Maximum extent of Roman Empire Pantheon built *Antoninus Pius Marcus Aurelius*	100
				200
			Diocletian Constantine the Great Christianization of Roman Empire Foundation of Constantinople (Istanbul) Split of Roman Empire into East and West *Constantius* *Julian the Apostate*	300
			Barbarian invasions of Italy	400